Salute
to Courage
Second Edition

A Beka Book® Pensacola, FL 32523-9100
an affiliate of PENSACOLA CHRISTIAN COLLEGE®

To Parents and Teachers

Children are eagerly searching for a workable sense of values. They need reading material that will give them ideals to reach for and examples to follow.

The stories in this reader have been selected from the readers of America's past and have been edited, modernized, and classroom-tested for student appeal and readability. Many character values are woven throughout the stories. Thought questions at the end of the stories aid in understanding the selections.

Salute to Courage
Second Edition

Staff Credits

Editors: Laurel Hicks, Marion Hedquist
Illustrators: Brian Jekel, Matthew Sample II, Stan Shimmin,
          Jonathan Taylor, and staff
Designer: Michelle Johnson

Cataloging Data
   Salute to courage / editor: Laurel Hicks et.al
      265 p. : col. ill. ; 22 cm. (A Beka Book reading program)
      1. Readers (Primary) 2. Reading (Primary) III. Hicks, Laurel.
IV. A Beka Book, Inc.
Library of Congress PE1119 .S37 2008
Dewey System 428.6

CONTENTS

*This story could be read during black history month.

Pronunciation Key

Symbol • Example		Symbol • Example	
ā	āte	ŏ	nŏt
â	dâre	oi	boil
ă	făt	o͞o	fo͞od
ä	fäther	o͝o	bo͝ok
ə	ago (ə·gō′)	ou	out
ē	ēven	th	thin
ĕ	ĕgg	~~th~~	~~th~~ere
ê (ər)	pondêr	tu̇	pictu̇re
ī	īce	ū	ūnit
ĭ	ĭt	û	hûrt
ō	ōver	ŭ	ŭp
ô	côrd, taught,
saw	zh	measure

Ronny, the Rope Climber

Arthur S. Maxwell

It happened in the gym one afternoon. Mr. Skinner, the gym teacher, was talking to a group of boys near the long ropes that dangled from the ceiling.

"This is the last time this year that we are going to try to beat the school record," he said, "and I hope one of you will do it. You have sometimes come very close to it. You must each try a little bit harder."

The boys knew exactly what he meant. The school record stood at 2.1 seconds for climbing 15 feet from a standing start. Bob had done it once in 2.5 seconds, Dick in 2.4 seconds, Jerry in 2.6 seconds, and Ronny in 2.2 seconds. But no one, so far, had even equaled the record.

"Ready!" called Mr. Skinner, stopwatch in hand. "Bob first. One, two, three, go!"

Leaping as high as he could, Bob grabbed the rope and shot up faster than a monkey. He touched the board at the 15-foot mark, then slid down again and waited anxiously to hear the result.

"Just under 2.4 seconds," said Mr. Skinner. "Good try, Bob, but it's not quite good enough. Let's see what Dick can do."

Dick leaped at the rope and flew up and down again in less time than it takes to tell of it. But he too was not fast enough. "Exactly 2.3 seconds," said Mr. Skinner. "Now Jerry."

---

stopwatch—*a watch that can be started and stopped instantly; used for timing races*

Jerry tried hard too, but didn't do any better than he had before.

"Well, Ronny, it's up to you," said Mr. Skinner. "All our hopes are on you now."

By this time quite a crowd of boys had drifted into the gym. All the school had heard about the rope contest and how near a few of the best climbers were to breaking the record. Now they pressed close to see what Ronny would do this time.

Ronny wanted to beat the record more than anyone there could guess. He wasn't the best of students. He never got very good grades, but he could climb a rope. And he thought that maybe this could be one way in which he could bring honor to the school he loved so much.

"Are you ready, Ronny?" asked Mr. Skinner.

"Ready," said Ronny.

"One, two, three, go!"

With a gleam in his eye and a grim look on his face, Ronny leaped at the rope. Hand over hand, he sped to the top. A moment later he was sliding down again.

"Two seconds!" shouted Mr. Skinner excitedly. "Well done, my boy! Well done!"

A cheer went up all over the gym. Ronny had beaten the record!

"But Mr. Skinner," Ronny said. "There's something I have to tell you."

"What is it, Ronny?" asked Mr. Skinner. All the boys leaned forward to hear what Ronny had to say.

"I'm afraid I didn't touch the marker. I missed it by about a half inch."

Only a half inch! And nobody had seen. Not even Mr. Skinner. It would have been so easy for Ronny to have let everyone think he had touched the marker. But though it meant losing the record, Ronny wouldn't purposely mislead the others.

Mr. Skinner took him by the hand and looked him straight in the eye. "I'm proud of you, Ronny," he said. "More proud than you will ever know. You have brought more glory to your school today by your honesty than you ever could by your rope climbing."

By this time all the boys were crowding around, wondering what would happen.

"Didn't he break the record?" several asked.

"No," said Mr. Skinner. "He climbed in two seconds, but he failed to touch the marker by a half inch. He is disqualified."

---

disqualified—*made not suitable or ineligible*

5

There were groans all over the gym. "What a shame!" cried some.

"Why didn't you keep your mouth shut, Ronny?" said others.

Mr. Skinner blew his whistle. As silence fell, he said, "Because of my inaccuracy, I am going to give Ronny one more chance."

Cheers rang out again, with shouts of "Do it this time, Ronny."

Ronny stepped to the rope.

"Take an extra-high leap," Mr. Skinner said.

Up went Ronny, faster than ever, his hand hitting the marker so everyone could see it. Down he came like a streak of lightning.

"Magnificent!" cried Mr. Skinner, clapping Ronny on the back. "You did it in 1.9 seconds and broke the record all to pieces!"

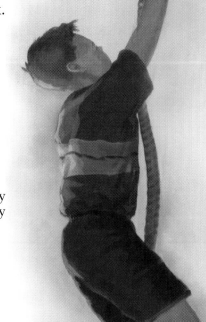

---

inaccuracy—*mistake; error*
magnificent—*excellent; superb*

Character Theme—Honesty
& Integrity

Thinking It Through

1. What was the school record for climbing 15 feet from a standing start?

2. Why was it so important to Ronny to beat the record?

3. What confession did Ronny make to Mr. Skinner after everyone thought he had beaten the record?

4. Why did Mr. Skinner give Ronny another chance to break the record?

5. When Ronny confessed to not touching the marker, did the other boys think he had made the right choice?

6. If Ronny had kept quiet about missing the marker, do you think he would have felt as proud about "breaking the record" as he did after he actually did break it? What other feelings may he have had?

From the Bible

Wherefore putting away lying, speak every man truth with his neighbor.
—*Ephesians 4:25*

Rosina's Chickens

Gladys Relyea

Rosina sat in the doorway of her very own chicken house. Carefully, she counted her chickens as they ate hungrily from the feeding-trays she had just filled with wet mash.

"Eighty-two . . . eighty-three . . ." she murmured. "But where is eighty-four?"

Worried, Rosina looked into the dimness of the chicken house.

"Here, chick, chick, chick," she called. "Please come and get your breakfast. It's almost time for me to go to school."

Rosina often talked that way to her chickens. And why shouldn't she? She had fed and watered her chickens and kept them warm and dry from the time they were pale-yellow balls of fluff only two days old.

Rosina (rō·zē′nə)

Now, three months later, they were ready to be sold. In fact, Rosina's father was to take them tomorrow to sell them in Springdale with his own chickens.

Again Rosina called. This time, number eighty-four ran from behind the chicken house and began to eat with the others.

Rosina sighed sadly, remembering that in exactly one day, she would have to say good-bye to them all.

"But, anyway, they'll sell for enough money for my Easter trip," she told herself. "And when I get back, I can start another batch."

The Easter trip to the wonderful St. Louis zoo! That had been Rosina's fondest dream ever since January when the teacher had told the class about it.

At last she would be able to see all the animals she had read about so often—the pandas, the lions, the boa constrictors!

"Rosie! It's 8:30!" came a call from the white farmhouse where she lived.

Rosina hurried back across the fields, scarcely giving a glance to her father's and her big

---

boa constrictor—*a large, nonpoisonous snake that crushes its prey*

brothers' hundreds of chickens. It wouldn't do to be late for school today, the last day before the Monday that meant St. Louis and the zoo.

In the cozy kitchen, Rosina picked up her lunch and kissed her mother good-bye. Then she banged down the porch steps and pedaled away on her blue bicycle.

In a few minutes, Rosina came to the tiny farm where Mrs. Fontini lived all alone. Mrs. Fontini was working in her chicken-yard.

Rosina and Mrs. Fontini were great friends. Even though Rosina was now ten, she still loved to play with the lovely doll which Mrs. Fontini had brought with her from northern Italy. The doll had real hair and was dressed exactly as a little Italian girl should be dressed.

"Good morning, Mrs. Fontini!" called Rosina, slowing down.

"Good morning, Rosina!" Mrs. Fontini answered. "Today I go to Springdale to grape-juice factory—I find work for summer maybe."

"I hope so," Rosina called back.

Soon, Rosina was in front of the Tonteretti farm, this one a big grape and chicken farm like her own.

In a moment, Mary Tonteretti dashed out,

Fontini (fän·tē′nē)   Tonteretti (tän·tûr′ĕt′ē)

and so did her brother Julio. They wheeled down the front lawn on their bicycles. Even Julio didn't want to be late so near the St. Louis zoo trip.

"Hey, Rosie, did you hear the news this morning?" asked Julio. "There was a tornado down in Oklahoma last night—a bad one."

"I hope we never have one here," Mary said with a shiver.

"Me, too," said Rosina. "It might kill my chickens."

"You and your chickens!" laughed Julio. "Think they were made of gold or something. I'd like to be in a tornado—wow! And wouldn't one of your chickens look funny with all the feathers blown off of it?"

Still laughing, Julio sped down the road ahead of them.

"Don't mind him, Rosie," said Mary. "He's always teasing me, too."

The two girls rode on down the dirt road between the neat farms with their rows of Concord grapevines, now just starting to bud out. And past the long chicken-houses where hundreds of young chickens scratched about. Everybody in this little Arkansas town raised chickens and grapes, it seemed.

Julio (jo͞o′lē·ō)

A few minutes later, Mary and Rosina turned cautiously onto the big road, riding close to the edge as they had been taught to do.

The last bell was ringing, and students from the first grade to the eighth were running or riding toward the little white schoolhouse next to the church buildings.

Classes that day went slowly for Rosina. Twice the teacher had to speak to her for dreaming instead of studying.

Finally at three o'clock, when the teacher gave the last instructions for the trip on Monday, Rosina thought she had never been so happy.

As soon as she could, she dashed out to her bicycle, not even waiting for Mary. What if something had happened to her eighty-four chickens while she'd been in school? What if the dog had broken into their yard? She pedaled hard toward home.

Without warning, something cold and brittle hit her on the nose as she turned off the highway. Then, whatever it was bounced off. Rosina looked up at the sky. Tiny hailstones were falling from dark, puffy clouds. Then, more hailstones hit her face—bigger ones.

---

hailstones—*little balls of ice that fall like rain*

"Oh, my poor chickens!" she gasped. "I closed their door—they can't get in!"

She passed the Tonteretti farm. She could see Mr. and Mrs. Tonteretti and the hired man running about closing up all their chicken houses. They must think there was going to be a bad storm. Did they expect a tornado like the one in Oklahoma?

She searched the clouds for the huge funnel like the picture she'd seen in the weather book. One enormous cloud off to the west did look ugly and purple. It curved and moved around like boiling syrup, but there was no long funnel.

Now Rosina was in front of Mrs. Fontini's little farm. Mrs. Fontini's red chickens were huddled together against their house. Their door was closed, too.

Rosina thought, "Why doesn't she let them in?" Then she remembered. Mrs. Fontini had gone to Springdale.

Rosina got off her bicycle and started to run toward the chicken house. There was a peculiar quiet everywhere and a strange yellow light. She looked again at the sky. The purple cloud was closer, and it had something long like an elephant's trunk hanging from it.

Rosina stopped running. "If that *is* a tornado cloud," she said aloud, "I'd better get home to my own chickens."

Her father and mother wouldn't know she had left the door closed. And they wouldn't notice it when they closed in their own chickens, because her chicken house was almost hidden behind the old barn.

Rosina ran back to her bicycle. At top speed, she headed toward her precious chickens. The elephant trunk was bigger now. It *must* be a tornado cloud!

Rosina's heart beat faster. Her chickens might get blown away or hit with something. And then how could she go to St. Louis? But Mrs. Fontini had only those chickens to pay for her living until the grapes were ready to be harvested in July. What would *she* do if they were killed?

Rosina's feet lagged on the pedals. Then she turned back. She just couldn't let Mrs. Fontini lose her chickens.

The dark funnel seemed almost above Rosina as she opened the door of the chicken house. Frantically, the chickens scurried in.

Now a heavy rain began to fall, and the wind blew hard. It was too late for Rosina to go home. It was even too late for her to run to Mrs. Fontini's "tornado cave" near the house. So she went inside with the chickens and closed the door.

Timidly, she watched the storm through the windows. "Oh, my poor little chickens," she thought. "They'll think I've forgotten them."

Rosina had heard what strange things a tornado can do. It can lift up a whole house and set it down.

She knew that a tornado wind can drive pieces of straw right into a tree-trunk. And once down in Texas, her father had told her, a tornado picked up a corncob and hit a cow on the head with it and stunned it.

Think what such wind could do to a soft little chicken! Rosina's eyes filled with tears; she just couldn't help it.

Outside, the wind and rain still beat against the chicken house. Then suddenly, all was quiet. The sun came out. Rosina opened the door cautiously. To the west, the sky was blue. To the east, the dark clouds hurried away.

Rosina ran to her bicycle. The dirt road was muddy, and the going was hard. And here and there, trees were lying on the road. But soon she was in her own driveway.

Then her mother hurried out of the kitchen. "Rosie," she cried, hugging her tightly. "Where have you been? Julio and Mary were home long ago."

Rosina pulled away. "I've got to see my chickens!" she said. "I left their door shut. They couldn't get out of the storm!"

"Rosie, wait!" said her mother. "Your chickens are safe. The whole town's safe. The foot of the funnel went through the woods."

Rosina was so happy that she took her mother by both hands and whirled her round and round.

"Rosie, stop!" said her mother. "Tell me— where were you during the storm?"

Rosina giggled. "I was in Mrs. Fontini's chicken house! She left the door closed, and I was afraid the tornado would carry her chickens away—and she needs them."

"Well done, my brave one," said her mother. "Mrs. Fontini will be grateful. Now come into the house and try on your new Easter dress."

"It will be my St. Louis zoo dress, too," Rosina said with a little skip up the steps.

Character Theme—Helpfulness, Sacrifice, & Unselfishness

Thinking It Through

1. How many chickens did Rosina have?
2. How did Rosina plan to use the money she would get when her chickens were sold?
3. Why was Mrs. Fontini going to the grape-juice factory in Springdale?
4. As Rosina left school, what was the first sign that a storm was on the way?
5. What kind of a storm struck that day?
6. What did Rosina do that showed she was unselfish?

The Grasshopper

Conrad Aiken

Grasshopper
grasshopper
all day long
we hear your scraping
summer song
    like
        rusty
            fiddles
                in
        the
      grass
as through
      the meadow
           path
            we pass
such funny legs
such funny feet
and how we wonder
what you eat
maybe a single blink of dew
sipped from a clover leaf would do
then high in air
    once more you spring
      to fall in grass again
          and sing.

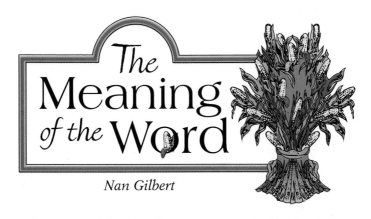

The Meaning of the Word

Nan Gilbert

"Re-spon-si-bil-i-ty," Peter spelled slowly. His blue eyes were tightly closed so he wouldn't see the dictionary page before him.

It was a mouthful of a word, and there wasn't much chance the teacher would get up to anything that size. Still, you never could tell what would happen when there were only two or three left in a spelling bee.

"Petey!" Ma called. "Your supper's getting cold."

Peter's brows drew together in a frown. "Ma, please don't call me that! You got all the fellows doin' it now!"

"Ah, now, you're still my little boy yet awhile!" his mother laughed, ruffling the hair that fell over his eyes. "Come on, you know so many words now, you'll spell down the teacher herself."

"Well, I better," Peter muttered. Only by some amazing feat like that could he hope to erase the laughter that followed him now around the schoolyard. "Oh, Pete-y, you mowed down any haystacks today?"

It had started way back in early fall. It was mid-November now, but nobody had forgotten. Ever since Peter's tenth birthday, he had begged to drive the tractor.

"Too young yet, Petey," his father kept saying. Even when Peter's eleventh birthday came and went, Pa just said, "Being grown-up is not something you measure with years."

Finally Pa showed him the workings of the tractor and let him make his first trial run. Peter felt like a king up there on the high tractor seat. He couldn't keep still about it. At school the next day, he bragged to everyone about the way he'd handled that machine.

Still, he wasn't so crazy about tractor-driving that he let it add to his chores. He stayed on at school in the afternoons playing ball. He knew Pa and his big brother Dirk were starting fall plowing and would have given him a turn at it, but he didn't want to miss his ball games.

He always got out to the fields by dusk to beg

feat—*a remarkable or unusual deed*

to drive a tractor back to the farmyard. Usually either Pa or Dirk welcomed the chance to walk and let Peter take the tractor in.

One evening some boys from Peter's school came bicycling past the farm just as Peter was driving the tractor down the lane inside the fence. Peter was keeping well behind the cows that were wandering toward the barn when he heard the whistles and yells from the road.

"Ride 'em, cowboy! Rope that there steer!" the boys called.

Peter yelled and waved in return. Sitting up a bit straighter, he shifted to a higher gear and closed in on the cows. He just couldn't resist the opportunity to show off.

The startled cows broke into a clumsy trot and came mooing and bellowing into the farm-yard. Peter circled them, swinging the tractor this way and that.

And then—he made the mistake of taking a peek out at the road to see how it was going over with the boys. Just five seconds of not watching where he was going, and—pow! He ran smack into the haystack!

Bundles of hay came rolling down on his head and shoulders. Hay got in his mouth and up his nose. He couldn't yell; he couldn't breathe.

He just kept driving deeper and deeper into the dusty, scratchy, solid heap until—

Whoof! In a cloud of dust and floating hay, he burst out the other side! The boys in the road laughed so hard they had to lean against each other for support.

That was the last tractor-driving Peter had done. He guessed it was the last he'd ever get to do till he was an old man with a white beard.

Pa had made him fork all the hay back into its pile. But that wasn't half as bad as going to school the next day.

Peter's ears burned, just remembering what the kids had said. He'd never live it down till he

fork—*place hay in a stack using a pitchfork*

did something to make headlines a different way, like winning this spelling bee. Well, he couldn't be any more ready, Peter guessed, closing the dictionary with a big sigh.

Outside the window, he could see Pa coming slowly up from the cornfield. Corn was the family's money crop, and everything had held it back this year. Not until late August had there been real corn weather. Now Pa was worried that the corn wouldn't dry enough before winter storms struck. The neighbors had all finished harvesting last week, but Pa's corn was slower. Harvest corn when it was too moist and it would spoil in the crib; they couldn't have that happen.

Peter went out to the kitchen, where supper was spread. Dirk was already eating with an open book beside his plate.

"Books! Books! I never thought to raise such a pair of bookworms!" Ma said, with pride in her voice. Dirk was in high school and captain of a debate team. Peter knew he had an important debate coming tomorrow.

"Hi, Petey," Dirk said absently.

Peter opened his mouth to protest and then shut it hastily. Next to Pa, Dirk was top man

---

money crop—*a crop raised by a farmer to sell for profit*
debate—*a contest where opposite viewpoints are argued*

around here; even Ma treated him with respect. How did he get that way, Peter wondered?

"Pa is out looking at the clouds again," Ma said.

"There's a blizzard north of us," said Dirk. "We're sure to get it."

"Not with the corn still in the field!" Ma gave a little anxious sigh and turned back to the stove.

Pa came in the back door. "Tomorrow we harvest," he said flatly. "The corn is ready, and it is foolish to take any more chance on the weather."

"Tomorrow?" yelped Peter, bouncing upright in his chair. "I can't miss school tomorrow. There's the spelling bee!"

Pa looked at him with stern disapproval. "Dirk is all the man I need," he said.

"But Dirk's got a de—" Peter broke off, silenced by his brother's cold glare. Well, all right, he was just trying to help Dirk out! A debate team wasn't much good without its captain, but if Dirk just didn't care—Why was everybody down on him all at once? Peter gobbled his supper and hiked up to his room. Families sure could be funny sometimes.

When Peter came down for breakfast the next morning, Pa and Dirk were already in the field. The air was cold and crisp, the sky clear.

Peter ate a big breakfast, skipped as many chores as he dared, and was ready for the walk to school by eight o'clock.

"Responsibility," he tried out his memory on one of the words he had studied yesterday. "Re-spon-si-bil-i-ty." Yep, he still remembered it.

Peter looked toward the field. Dirk was waiting to unhitch the loaded wagon of corn from the picker, but Pa hadn't started down the next row of corn. He was driving his tractor lickity-bump up to the barnyard.

Low on gas, Peter guessed. Now Pa leaped off and dragged the hose toward the tractor.

"Pa!" called Peter, remembering the first lesson Pa had taught him about the tractor. "Pa, you didn't turn off your engine!"

Faster than the words, it happened. One second there was Pa holding the nozzle over the funnel, and the next second there was flame rising up in a red curtain.

Then, as suddenly, it was over. Dirk was off to the house for oil and soft cloths, and Ma was gently ripping the shirt-sleeves from Pa's burned arms.

Quiet, soft-spoken Ma had become a commanding general, taking prompt, efficient charge.

---

lickity-bump—*quickly*
nozzle—*spout at the end of a hose*

efficient—*working well; effective*

Now she backed the car from the garage and helped Pa to the seat beside her.

"Best to run you right in to the hospital," she said firmly.

Dirk stepped close to the car. "We'll stick by the corn, Pa," he said, his voice very steady and confident. "We'll get it in okay. Won't we, Pete?"

Peter gulped. Warmth crept back into the tight ball of his stomach. He looked at Dirk with gratitude. Dirk had called him Pete! And there was something he could do for Pa after all.

"Sure," Peter said shakily. "Sure, we'll make out fine, Pa."

He saw Pa's eyes shining back at them, warmly, proudly, as Ma swished down the drive.

"Let's get going, Pete," Dirk said briskly. "I'll take the cornpicker. You handle the tractor. Okay?"

The tractor? Dirk was giving him the tractor without even a crack about keeping the straw out of his hair? Well, Peter would show him that he could be trusted. Driving carefully, Peter chugged back to the cornfield.

"Ought to run ninety bushels an acre," Dirk said, unhooking the wagon and putting the

acre—*a section of land*

26

empty in its place. He sounded just as though he was talking to Pa.

"Yeh," agreed Peter, striving to be equally man-to-man. "Sure looks good."

Why, this was man's work he was doing, Peter thought, his chest expanding. This was grown-upness. This was what went with the name of Pete.

Far off, the school-bell tinkled. Peter remembered the spelling bee for which he'd prepared so hard, and disappointment hit him so keenly it hurt. Then he shrugged it off. A spelling bee was kid stuff beside this!

As the morning hours dragged on, Peter's glow wore off, and plain aching tiredness took its place. On the cornpicker, Dirk was more and more silent.

Occasionally, Dirk glanced at the sky. Peter looked, too, but there was nothing to see but a dab of cloud on the north horizon that he could cover with his hand.

Back and forth. Hitch on, unload, bounce back to the field. How little corn they had picked compared to all that waited! Peter gave a big tired sigh and looked at the cloud again. He put his hand against it, and the cloud mushroomed all around it.

---

grown-upness—*act of being like an adult*

mushroomed—*grew quickly*

"Hey, Dirk!" Peter called uneasily, "It's getting bigger!"

Dirk didn't ask him what he meant. He'd been watching, too. "Be here by dark," he said briefly.

Peter looked at the untouched rows of corn. "Dirk, we can't finish it!" he cried.

"Nope," Dirk answered, not stopping. "But we'll get all we can."

It was a losing battle, and Peter was ready to cry with weariness, but he couldn't quit. Every extra ear of corn counted.

Suddenly, he straightened and stared un-believingly out at the road. What kind of crazy parade was that coming? It was a long, crawling worm with giraffe heads shooting up every few feet! It bobbled and swayed and curved right up to the gate!

At the edge of the field, Dirk gave a great shout. "Pete, they're coming to help us—all the neighbors! Look at 'em! Seven, eight, nine cornpickers! More than two dozen tractors and wagons!" Dirk's voice choked up. He dropped off the picker and gave Peter a big hug. "We've got it licked, Pete! We'll beat the blizzard. We got it licked!"

There were tears in his eyes, and tears rolling down Peter's cheeks, and neither boy cared who saw them.

"Heard about your Pa's accident," Mr. Hoffman said kindly. "The boys here thought we'd better give you a hand; sky doesn't look too good." He gazed out over the harvested acres. "You kids already do this much? You've really been working!"

"Pete here helped fine," Dirk said. "Good as a man."

"I can see that," Mr. Hoffman nodded. He gave Peter a keen glance. "Guess there's enough of us to handle the unloading now. Why don't you knock off and get yourself a breath, Pete? You've done a man's job today."

Gratefully, Peter staggered toward the back steps while the long row of cornpickers slashed into the waiting rows of corn with a mighty roar.

Let the cloud grow now; let the blizzard come—the corn would be harvested before dark!

"A man's job." That's what he'd done. For six weary hours, he'd been grown-up. And he'd found out what that long word he'd mastered yesterday meant. Re-spon-si-bil-i-ty.

He'd missed the spelling bee, and Dirk his debate, because they felt responsible for their family. All these men had left their own work because they felt responsible for their neighbors. Why, Pa was right! Grown-upness wasn't measured by years; it was measured by the number of people you felt you needed to help!

The car came bumping into the driveway, and Ma hopped out, her face tired but shining.

"Pa's fine!" she called happily to Peter. "They'll let him come home in no time. And oh, Petey, the neighbors came, didn't they? Bless them, they'll want coffee and such; I'll go fix it."

She bustled off, and Peter was left with his mouth open. Suddenly he didn't mind the baby name; he even liked it a little. It proved he still had time to work on this big business of grown-upness.

His work done, Peter felt like heading to the couch with a couple of apples to crunch on and a good book to read. Nobody could say he hadn't earned a rest.

But his eyes went from Dirk still in the field to his mother hurrying to the kitchen. It was plain to Peter that once you let a big word like *responsibility* get into your veins, you couldn't ever quite shake it loose again.

"Ma," Peter called, trailing her into the kitchen. "You want any chores done?"

Character Theme—Family & Responsibility

Thinking It Through

1. What school event was Peter preparing for?
2. Why was it so important to Peter to win the spelling bee?
3. What was the family's money crop?
4. Why did Pa decide to harvest corn the next day?
5. What happened when Pa started to put gas into the tractor with the engine running?
6. Who came to help Pete and Dirk get all of the corn in before the blizzard hit?
7. What word did Pete learn the meaning of?

Something
Told the Wild Geese
Rachel Field

Something told the wild geese
   It was time to go.
Though the fields lay golden
   Something whispered, "Snow."
Leaves were green and stirring,
   Berries, luster-glossed,
But beneath warm feathers
   Something cautioned, "Frost."

All the sagging orchards
   Steamed with amber spice,
But each wild breast stiffened
   At remembered ice.
Something told the wild geese
   It was time to fly—
Summer sun was on their wings,
   Winter in their cry.

---

luster-glossed—*bright and shiny*
amber—*brownish-yellow*

Little THINGS

Julia Fletcher Carney

Little drops of water,
   Little grains of sand,
Make the mighty ocean
   And the pleasant land.

So the little moments,
   Humble though they be,
Make the mighty ages
   Of eternity.

So our little errors
   Lead the soul away
From the path of virtue,
   Far in sin to stray.

Little deeds of kindness,
   Little words of love,
Help to make earth happy
   Like the heaven above.

On the
Mayflower

Enid LaMonte Meadowcroft

The *Mayflower* rocked and tossed on the waves. In the sky a black cloud grew larger and larger. Lightning flashed. The wind whistled and cried.

"Get below, Giles Hopkins," called a man as he ran along the deck. He stopped to speak to a boy who held fast to the railing.

"I don't mind getting wet," the boy answered. "It's so crowded in the cabin, and half the people are seasick."

"Never mind that. It's not safe here. And you are in the way."

"Let me help then, Master Howland. I'm big enough," said Giles. But John Howland had already turned to go.

Suddenly the rain came. The boat tipped until she seemed to be lying on her side. The deck slanted so that the boy could hardly stand. He clung to the railing and shut his eyes to keep out the sight of the water. When he looked again, the

---

Giles (jīlz)

34

boat had righted herself. But John Howland had disappeared.

Giles ran to the side of the vessel. There was his friend in the water, splashing and yelling. A great wave rolled over his head and seemed to swallow him.

On the deck at the boy's feet lay a coil of rope. One end of it hung over the side of the ship.

"The rope! Grab the rope!" called Giles. He saw Master Howland grasp it and then disappear again under another wave.

Giles turned and ran down the deck. "Help!" he yelled. "Help! Help! Man overboard!"

Several of the sailors came running in answer to his cry. They grabbed the rope and pulled on it. John Howland still clung to the other end. But it was a long rope, and he was far from the ship. The men pulled him through the water as

though he were a fish. Then slowly, slowly they
pulled him up the side of the boat. He dangled
at the end of the rope like a wet rag doll. The
angry waves beat against him.

Then one of the sailors grabbed a large boat
hook. He reached over the side of the ship and
caught it in Howland's clothes. So with the rope
and the hook they tugged and pulled until they
had him safe on board.

"Oh!" gasped John Howland when he could
speak. "I have been nearer land than any of
you. And I have swallowed most of the ocean.
There can't be much left between us and America
now."

Then he saw Giles standing near. The boy's
hair lay flat on his head. Water streamed down
his face and clothes. He was as wet as if he too
had been overboard.

"You saved my life, boy," said Howland. "If
you hadn't brought help it would have been the
end of me. I couldn't have held on another minute. Now will you go below?"

"Yes, sir," said Giles, as he started down the
ladder to the cabin.

It was almost dark in the cabin. The little
ship still rolled and tossed. It was not yet safe
to light the oil lamps or the candles.

All day the ship had been thrown about by the great waves. Everything in the cabin was upset. Boxes and cases would not stay in place. They slid back and forth across the cabin floor with each toss of the ship.

Some of the littlest children cried with fear. Many of them had been fastened in their bunks so that they would not be hurt by the sliding boxes or be thrown to the floor when the ship pitched.

The older children took care of the younger ones. Or they sat on benches at the long table in the center of the room and told each other stories.

Many of the women lay in their bunks too ill to move. Others who were well enough tried to care for them. They clung to the bunks and to the table as they walked about. They tried to keep away from sliding boxes and ran into each other.

Giles went to his mother, who sat on the edge of her bunk. A little girl was asleep in her lap.

"Where have you been, my son?" asked Mistress Hopkins. "I sent your sister to look for you some time ago. But Constance said she could not find you. You are very wet. What have you been doing?"

---

pitched—*tossed forward and backward*

"I was on the main deck," the boy answered. "Master Howland slipped and fell overboard. But he grabbed a rope that hung over the side, and we pulled him up. They have taken him to the steerage to dry him out. I was the one who called for help. He said I saved his life," Giles added proudly.

"Then I suppose it is a good thing you were there," said Mistress Hopkins." Though I heard your father tell you to stay below today. Now change your clothes at once. There are some dry ones in our box if you can find it. I saw it slide under Mistress White's bunk a minute ago. If I move to help you, little Mary will wake, and she has just dropped off to sleep. Her poor mother is much too ill to care for her."

"It seems to me that almost everyone is sick," said Giles. "I'm glad the sea doesn't make me feel that way. I'm hungry."

"You'll get little to eat tonight, my boy. Just a bit of smoked beef and some bread. No one has been able to light a fire all day. With the boat pitching so, it is not safe. Hurry now and get yourself dry, or you will be sick too," said Mistress Hopkins.

"Yes, Mother," replied Giles. He pulled the box from under a bunk near by. Then he took out

steerage—*the part of the ship for passengers paying the lowest fares*

some dry clothes and went to the men's quarters to change.

After several days the rain stopped. The wind died down, and the sea was calm. It was cold, but the sun shone. Sails were raised again, and the *Mayflower* sped on her way across the ocean.

Everyone felt better. The children had been shut up in the cabin for many days. Just to see and feel the sun made them race about the decks and shout for joy.

The women called back and forth to each other as they hung damp clothes out to dry. The sailors sang as they hammered down the hatches and coiled ropes.

Some of the boys were playing soldier on the main deck. Wrestling Brewster was the leader. He had often watched the men as they drilled every day under Captain Standish.

As they played, they saw Constance Hopkins running toward them. "Guess what has happened! Oh, guess!" she cried. "I have a new baby brother. He was born last night. Mother just let me hold him for a minute."

"A baby brother," said Love Brewster. "What is his name?"

---

hatch—*a covering over a hole that leads from one deck of a ship to another*

"It's a funny name," answered Constance. "Mother is going to call him Oceanus because he was born on the ocean. My big brother, Giles, is making a cradle for him out of an empty case."

"Oceanus Hopkins," said Wrestling. "That is quite a name. Perhaps I can help Giles with the cradle or make a box to hold his clothes."

"Now there are four of us; Giles, Damaris, Oceanus, and me," said Constance. "Oh, Wrestling," she added, "I forgot to tell you that your mother said your dinner was ready. She says you must hurry, for the food is hot this noon."

"Hurray! Come on, Love," said Wrestling. The two boys started off to find their mother.

Hot food was a real treat on the *Mayflower*. There were only two ways in which it could be cooked, and both ways were hard. It could be put in a frying pan and held over a charcoal fire. Or it could be cooked in a kettle hung on an iron tripod, over a fire made in a box of sand.

Each day the food was taken from a common store. Even the smallest children knew that the food they carried on the boat must last them a long time. No one knew how long it might be before there would be any more.

Oceanus (ō′shē·ă′nŭs)
Damaris (də·mâr′ĭs)

tripod—*a three-legged support*

Wrestling found
his mother standing
over a steaming kettle in the shelter of the
cookhouse. She was dishing food into a wooden
trencher.

"It is a good stew, my son," she said when she
saw Wrestling. "Dried beef, cabbage, turnips, and
onions have gone into the making of it. After such
terrible days of storm, we all need something to
make us strong. Take this for yourself and for Love."
She held out a trencher filled with steaming stew.

"Thank you," said Wrestling. "It looks good, and
I am so hungry." He reached for the wooden dish.

"Wait," said his mother, setting the dish beside
her. "I have just remembered the Hopkins children.
With a new baby to care for, Mistress Hopkins will

trencher—*a wooden board or
platter used for serving food*

not be cooking for a few days. Go and get them, Wrestling. Ask them to share our dinner with us."

"May we eat out here on deck, Mother?" asked Love as Wrestling ran to get Giles and his sisters.

"Of course you may," said his mother. "And so will everyone else. It is so good to see the sun again."

In a few minutes the children sat together on the deck. Wrestling and Love dipped their spoons into the same trencher. Giles shared his with Constance, and Mistress Brewster fed Damaris. There was little talking and a great deal of eating. Everyone was happy.

There were sunny days and stormy ones, but still the little *Mayflower* sailed the sea. Everyone was very tired of seeing nothing but water on all sides.

"We have been on this boat exactly sixty-three days," said Constance one afternoon. She and Giles were leaning against the railing watching the water. "I know how long it is, because I counted this morning while I was waiting for everyone to wake up."

Wrestling, who stood near by, sighed deeply. "Sometimes I don't believe we'll ever reach land," he said. "My mother said last night that she wished we were back in Holland."

"Does she?" asked Giles. He looked carefully at the water. Then he pointed excitedly.

"Look!" he cried. "Do you see that?"

"What?" asked Constance. "Oh, that's only a dead tree branch. What do you care about that?"

"Silly!" said Giles. "Do trees grow in the ocean?"

"Look! Look! Come here," he called to some of the crew who were working near by. The sailors dropped their work and ran to his side.

"There—a tree branch!" exclaimed Giles. "It means land is near, doesn't it?"

In a minute the deck was crowded with excited passengers. All were eager to see the first sign of land. Long after the tree branch had floated past them, they talked about it.

"Watch for birds now," said one of the sailors. "If you see a wild duck or a goose, you will know that we are really near the land."

So everyone who was able spent the rest of the day on deck. Each hoped to be the first one to sight land. But no one even saw a bird. At last it grew dark, and the children were sent below.

"Perhaps that branch came from a tree on an island, and we have sailed past it," thought

Constance sadly that night. She crawled into the bunk beside her little sister and was soon asleep.

But all night long on the boat, men kept watch. Eyes peered eagerly into the darkness. There was much talk of what the next day would bring. Hearts were lighter, for surely now they were near their journey's end.

It was very early the next morning that the cry rang out, "Land ho! Land ho!" It woke all who were asleep in the cabin.

Men, women, and children rushed to the decks. The morning air was cold, and they drew their cloaks about them. They peered into the distance.

Yes—there it was. At first it was only a dim shadow on the horizon. Then as the *Mayflower* sailed closer, rocks and trees appeared.

Everyone was excited. Everyone was happy. The children talked together and planned what they would do when they got off the boat.

But the sailors shook their heads. It was land—but it was not the end of their journey. They knew that the land they saw was Cape Cod. They were far north of the Hudson River, where they had planned to go.

So they turned the ship south and sailed along the coast. About noon they came to dangerous waters. They were afraid the boat would be wrecked in the breakers.

Then the captain and the men held a meeting, and they decided to turn back to Cape Cod. All the afternoon they sailed north along the coast. When the children went to bed that night the ship was still moving through the water.

Early, early the next morning Giles woke and lay still for a moment wondering why he felt so strange. Suddenly he knew that the ship was not rushing through the water any longer.

He called Wrestling and the two boys hurried to the deck. The *Mayflower* was at anchor in Cape Cod Bay. Soon all the Pilgrims were gathered on the deck.

Before them lay a new land. No friends were there to welcome them. There were no houses to shelter them and no stores where they could buy their food.

When they looked toward the shore, they could see only rocks, sand, and a forest of trees. What might be hiding there? It was winter, cold and stormy.

Yet no one said he was afraid. No one said he wanted to go back to his home in Holland or in England.

Together they knelt on the deck and thanked God because He had brought them safely to this land, where they could live as they thought He wanted them to. Then they began to plan at once for their new homes.

They were a brave people!

Character Theme—Courage

Thinking It Through

1. Why did John Howland say that Giles had saved his life?

2. Why couldn't the lamps or candles be lit on the lower decks during the storm?

3. What was the name of the baby who was born aboard the *Mayflower?*

4. What ocean did the Pilgrims cross to reach America?

5. Why was everyone so excited about a tree branch?

6. What did the Pilgrims do when they saw land?

The Will and the Way

Author Unknown

There's something I'd have you remember, boys,
  To help in the battle of life;
It will give you strength in the time of need
  And help in the hour of strife.
Whenever there's something that should be done,
  Don't be a coward, and say,
"What use to try?" Remember, then,
  That "where there's a will there's a way."

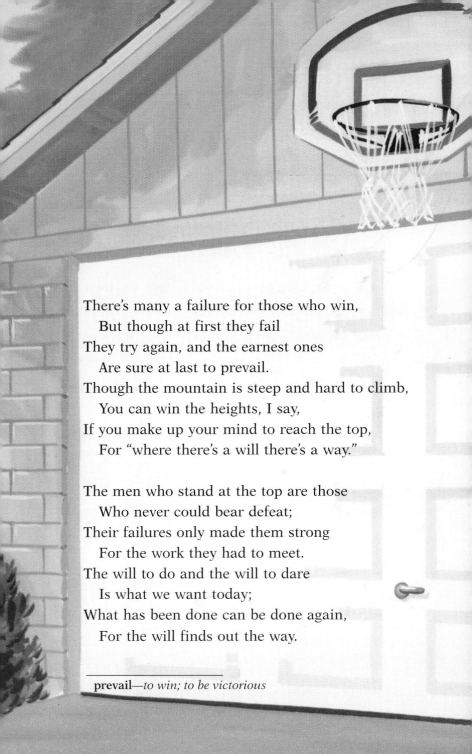

There's many a failure for those who win,
 But though at first they fail
They try again, and the earnest ones
 Are sure at last to prevail.
Though the mountain is steep and hard to climb,
 You can win the heights, I say,
If you make up your mind to reach the top,
 For "where there's a will there's a way."

The men who stand at the top are those
 Who never could bear defeat;
Their failures only made them strong
 For the work they had to meet.
The will to do and the will to dare
 Is what we want today;
What has been done can be done again,
 For the will finds out the way.

---

prevail—*to win; to be victorious*

Jungle Adventure

Alden G. Stevens

Each morning Simba would leave his own village and hurry through the jungle to the camp of the missionaries. When the sun was barely two hours high, he would hide among the ferns by the riverbank. There he would watch the strange things that the missionaries did.

There were two men and a woman, and there was a boy of about Simba's age, with hair as bright as sunshine.

From his hiding place on the opposite side of the river, Simba studied every move that the boy made.

One day, Simba heard the lady call the boy "Jack." Simba whispered the name that sounded so strange to him—"Jack."

One morning, while Simba lay watching from the jungle shadows, he saw the two men leave

---

Simba (sĭm′bə)

50

with the gun bearers. Jack sat down and began sharpening his knife. When he was finished, he walked restlessly about the camp for a few minutes, and then wandered off into the jungle.

Quickly Simba slipped from his hiding place. He darted through the thick ferns until he was directly across the river from Jack. Then, like some far-off shadow, he followed the boy, who tramped along noisily on the opposite bank.

Suddenly Simba froze up against the trunk of a great tree. Jack was coming toward him, wading across the stream in the shallows below the pool. Simba could feel the beat of his heart, racing as though he had run far and fast.

Now he and the boy were on the same side of the river—closer to each other than they had ever been before.

Something told Simba that he should not let the boy go alone in the jungle. And so he followed Jack closely. Once he was nearly discovered. He stopped, then, and waited for a few moments to let Jack get farther ahead of him.

Then he crept along again. At the edge of a clearing, he stopped and peered out from behind the leaves.

gun bearer—*person who carried the gun*

In the center of the clearing, a big rock jutted up about twenty feet above the ground. Jack was wandering slowly toward this rock from the other side.

All at once something else in the clearing caught Simba's eye, and his breath hissed inward in a gasp of terror. Not far from where he was standing, a huge buffalo was grazing.

Because he was coming from behind the rock, Jack could not see the buffalo. But soon he would step into sight, and the buffalo would see him.

Simba knew that buffaloes in a herd often gallop away at the sight of an enemy. But a lone buffalo bull would charge. Before Jack could make a move to climb the rock, the beast would thunder down upon him. Beneath those powerful hoofs, and torn by those sharp black horns, Jack would die.

Simba realized instantly that he alone could save Jack. Somehow, he must draw the beast's attention to himself before Jack came out from behind the rock.

But the trees around him were too big to climb. Ropy vines hung from their branches. Simba knew he could climb up these quickly, but if the buffalo were to charge them, they would break like strings.

---

terror—*intense fear*   lone—*only one*

He turned and looked again at the clearing. If he did not act soon, it would be too late. Suddenly he noticed a tall tree that grew near the edge of the clearing. He was a little nearer to it than the buffalo was.

A slender branch, which was well above the ground, grew straight out from the trunk of the tree. Simba saw then what he must do. It would be a close race, deadly close, but it was the only way he could save the boy's life.

Simba stepped at once into the clearing, calling out the strange name he had whispered to himself—"Jack! Jack! Jack!" Jack heard the warning cry, and stood staring at Simba, open-mouthed.

The startled buffalo heard the cry, too. He lifted his great head and gazed questioningly at this unexpected enemy.

Simba raised his bow. The feather of the arrow swept his cheek. Then the arrow flew toward the gray-black beast.

When he felt the prick of the arrowhead, the buffalo gave an angry bellow and swept toward Simba at a terrible speed. With the buffalo's hoofs thundering in his ears, Simba ran as he had never run before.

Nearer, nearer to the
tree Simba raced. Then he leaped.
His desperate fingers clutched at the slender
branch. As his body swung upward, the buffalo
passed beneath him. And the wind of his passing
was like the chill of death.

Jack had scrambled up the side of the rock
by now. He sat on the top, looking across at
Simba, sitting in the tree. The buffalo, roaring
angrily, stood guard between the two.

Now that the terrible danger was past, Jack
wanted to thank this stranger for saving his life.
"Say!" he shouted, "You're the fastest runner I
ever saw! I guess I would have been deader than
a door nail if it hadn't been for you!"

Simba's stomach felt weak with the excitement and relief. The boy was talking to him; it would be only polite to answer.

So, in the quick, singing rhythm of his own language, he shouted back at Jack. Jack did not know what Simba was saying, and Simba did not know what Jack was saying. But it was fun, anyway, talking back and forth.

The angry bellowing of the buffalo reminded the boys suddenly that they must call for help. They shouted together.

Jack had been missed from the camp, and the boys heard an answering shout almost at once. Then, for a moment, all was silent.

The two boys sat waiting anxiously, looking down at the buffalo below. He stood with his great head raised, sniffing the air, while his sharp eyes searched the jungle for any new enemies.

Suddenly a gun roared nearby, and the huge beast crashed to the grass.

As he went down, one of the missionaries stepped out from the jungle. At his heels were his two gun bearers. They moved watchfully toward the fallen buffalo, eyeing him carefully for signs of life. But the giant body did not stir. He was dead.

Then the missionary shouted, and at once the jungle air was filled with the cries and calls of many voices. The porters and gun bearers crowded into the clearing, all chattering excitedly. Then Jack's mother and father rushed in.

Carefully Jack and Simba climbed down, the one from his rock, the other from his tree.

Jack had scarcely touched the ground, when his mother caught him in her arms.

Frightened with the noise and excitement, Simba started to slip away into the jungle. But the tall missionary grabbed him by the arm and led him into the circle, where Jack and his parents stood.

"That's the boy, Mother!" cried Jack, pointing at Simba. "That's the boy who saved my life!" Then Jack told them what had happened. He looked at Simba admiringly. "I never saw anyone run so fast in all my life!"

Then Jack's father turned to one of the gun bearers and asked him to question Simba in his own language.

Simba told them how, for many days, he had watched the missionaries' camp. And he told them how he had followed Jack when he left the camp today.

Then, quite simply, he said, "When I saw that the boy was soon to die, I stepped out from where I was hidden. The buffalo chased me to the tree. The boy climbed up the rock to safety. That is all. I am finished talking."

As his listeners followed the story, looking at the rock and then at the tree, they realized how narrowly Simba had escaped death.

Jack's father was puzzled. Why should Simba risk his life to save a boy he didn't even know? He turned to the gun bearer and said, "Ask the boy why he did this thing."

When the gun bearer asked Simba this question, the boy thought for a moment. Then he said quietly, "In my village, there is a man who is a teller of stories. He is very wise. Once he told me, 'Great danger makes all men brothers.'

"When I saw that Jack was in great danger, he became my brother, and I did what I did."

Character Theme—Courage, Resourcefulness, & Sacrifice

Thinking It Through

1. Why did Simba follow Jack into the jungle?

2. What animal was Simba afraid would attack and perhaps kill Jack?

3. What did Simba do to distract the buffalo's attention away from Jack?

4. When Jack's father asked why Simba was willing to risk his life for Jack, what answer did Simba give?

Indian Summer

Cornelia Meigs

Richard Fowler's heart was beating fast with excitement. He held tightly to the sides of the small boat as the two sailors guided it toward the rocky New England shore.

In the harbor behind him, Dick could still see the ship *Mary Belinda* which had been his home for so many weeks. And ahead, beyond the rocks that lined the shore, he could see nothing but snow-covered hills and bare, unbroken woods.

It made a cold, unfriendly looking picture in the sunless light of that October morning.

But to Dick it was wonderful and exciting, and he wanted to stay here in America. It puzzled him that, after sailing for so many weeks to get here, the leaders of the company now thought it unwise to stay.

Last night they had sat for hours in the ship's cabin, trying to decide whether or not they should return to England.

And now, this very minute, they were meeting again.

Dick sighed. It seemed unfair that winter should come so early this year. The colonists had hoped for a few more weeks of good weather to get their settlement started.

The little boat had entered a small, sandy bay, and was now just a few yards from shore.

Dick helped the two sailors beach the boat and lift out the heavy wooden casks which they had brought to fill with fresh water. Then they left all the casks on the beach and began looking about for a spring.

"No need for you to stay with us," the men told Dick. "Go and do a little exploring, if you've a mind to. We have to take these casks of water to the ship and then come back for another load. We'll pick you up on our next trip, in about two hours."

Dick was off at once, up the hillside and into the woods. He climbed one hill and then another. He stopped to look at some animal tracks. Then he turned aside to pick some bright red berries that showed through the snow.

It was like a holiday, being on land again after all those weeks at sea. He hurried gaily on, forgetting to notice which way he was going.

When Dick finally decided that it was time to turn back, he realized, in a flash of fear, that he was lost.

All about him there were hills and crowded trees. There was no sign anywhere of the gray stretch of sea.

_____

cask—*barrel*

Suddenly he spotted a drift of smoke just a few yards away. He ran toward it quickly, burst through the brush, and stood breathless at the edge of a small clearing.

Before him, facing in the other direction, were a boy and a girl of about his own age. They were on their knees before a hollow log, from which smoke curled upward through the trees.

A twig snapped under Dick's foot. The boy and girl jumped up quickly, whirling about to face him. Dick realized with a start that they were Indians.

For a brief moment, the three of them stood staring at one another in surprise. Then the girl said something excitedly to the boy, and turned back to her work.

They were stuffing handfuls of wet moss into the opening of the hollow log, and Dick understood at once what they were doing. They had made a fire in the mouth of the log, perhaps to smoke out some animal which had hidden there.

Then the blaze had started to get out of control, and they were trying to put it out. The snow-covered moss that grew everywhere was almost as good as water for fighting fire.

---

start—*a surprised reaction*

Dick knew nothing about forest fires. But he could see that the boy and girl were working desperately to keep the fire from spreading to the pine trees all around.

Darting across the clearing, Dick grabbed a handful of the moss and pushed it into the flaming opening.

The Indian boy brushed by Dick, touching his shoulder as he pushed his own armload of wet moss into the blazing log.

A boy and girl could never have worked fast enough. But with the three of them all working together, they slowly began to win the battle. Finally the fire died down to a small glow.

The Indian boy leaned back, a smile of relief on his face. Then he swung about to face Dick and spoke a word which the white boy understood.

"English?" he asked.

Dick realized at once that both of these Indian children must have spent some time at the English colony not far from here. Between them, they knew several English words and had little trouble in understanding Dick's answers.

The girl, while she nodded and smiled, brought out a strip of dried deer meat and a bark cup full of berries.

Seeing the food made Dick realize suddenly that he had grown quite hungry. He sat down between the boy and girl and began to eat eagerly.

With signs and the small amount of English that the Indian pair could understand, the three talked together. They told Dick that their village was just beyond the next hill.

"Would the strangers make a camp for themselves on the shore?" the Indian boy asked.

"No," answered Dick sadly. Then he explained how his family and a few of their friends had left England late in June to come to America.

Because they were all poor, the only ship they could afford to hire was the slow-moving *Mary Belinda*. And they had been so long in coming, that now winter was already upon them. They would have to give up their great adventure and go back where they could be sure of food and shelter.

The Indian boy stared at Dick for a moment, shaking his head. Then he said, very clearly, "Summer comes again."

"That is true," Dick agreed. "But the long, cold winter must pass before there will be summer once more."

The Indian boy shook his head again. He held up three fingers, then five. "Days," he said.

"In three, maybe five, days, the summer comes again. Only little summer, maybe two, three weeks. *Then* comes snow."

Dick sat staring at them, longing to believe what he had heard, but afraid he might not have understood correctly.

Then he scrambled excitedly to his feet. The Indian boy stood up, too. "English boat that way," he said, pointing. "Tell friends summer comes again."

Half a mile from the beach, Dick met the sailors from the *Mary Belinda*. And as they rowed back toward the ship, he told them what he had learned.

Meanwhile, the men in the cabin of the *Mary Belinda* were still trying to decide whether to go or to stay.

At last Master John Fowler pushed back his chair. "I fear we must give up all our hopes," he said. "One month of good weather would give us time to build shelters. But with winter already here . . . ." He stopped at the sound of a noise outside.

Hurrying feet came stamping down the ladder, and the door burst open.

"Father!" Dick cried. "It's not really winter! The Indians say that in a few days it will be like summer again!"

Master John Fowler stared at his son in disbelief. "Like summer again?" he repeated.

"Yes!" Dick cried. "It will grow warm again for two or three weeks. In this country, summer comes again!"

67

John Fowler threw his arm around his son. "Ah, Richard! That is good news indeed!" he cried happily.

But his voice was drowned out by the joyful shouts of the other colonists. "Another summer! Summer comes again!"

A little more than a year later, the small colony of settlers beside the bay celebrated their first harvest. The short season which they now spoke of as the "Indian's Summer," had given them time to prepare for that first cold winter.

And now that they had had a good harvest, they were doing as the other colonists had done. They were setting aside a day to thank God for helping them in their undertaking.

When the sun showed that it was nearly noon, Dick Fowler left his settlement, where preparations were being made for the big Thanksgiving feast. He was carrying a loaf of bread. And in his pocket, he had put a handful of corn.

At a certain familiar clearing in the nearby hills, Dick stopped. A big log there still showed the marks of a burned-out fire.

Dick waited. In a little while, two quick-moving figures came silently out of the woods to stand beside him.

They laid three strips of dried deer meat, their share of the meal, on the log beside Dick's handful of corn. Then the three friends sat down to eat their own Thanksgiving dinner together—three Americans within the circle of the snow-covered pines.

Character Theme—Helpfulness & Friendship

Thinking It Through

1. On what ship did Richard Fowler sail to America?
2. Why had two sailors from the ship come ashore?
3. How long did it take the *Mary Belinda* to cross the Atlantic Ocean?
4. Why were the colonists debating whether or not to go back to England?
5. How did Dick help the Indian boy and girl put out the fire in the hollow log?
6. What good news did the Indian boy and girl give Dick?

Pocahontas

Eleanor and Herbert Farjeon

POCAHONTAS
Gentle and wild,
The Indian Chief
Powhatan's child,
In her deerskin-shoes
And her feather-cloak
Lived in Virginia
With her folk.

1595–1617

The red-leaf'd maple,
The pine-tree strong,
The wild-bee's honey,
The oriole's song,
The arrow's whistle,
The victim's yell,
Pocahontas
Knew these things well.

But when the White Men
Sought her land,
These she did not
Understand;
They came like heroes
Of ancient myth,
And when she saw him
She loved John Smith.

Powhatan (pou·ə·tăn′)
myth—*a legend; an imaginary story*

The Indian called
The White Man foe,
But Pocahontas
Did not so;
From the tomahawk
And the scalping-knife
Powhatan's daughter
Saved John Smith's life.

For when her idol
Was doomed to die
And bowed his head
As the blade rose high,
Her own brown body
On his she flung
And death was stayed
As the ax-head swung.

And did she wed
The man she saved?
Her story was not
So engraved.
John Rolfe, the settler,
Made her his bride,
And brought her to England,
Where she died.

But Pocahontas
In memory runs
Under Virginia's
Moons and suns,
Swift and eager,
Gentle and wild,
The Indian Chief
Powhatan's child.

Character Theme—Friendship &
Compassion

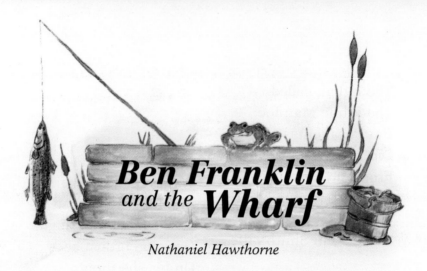

Ben Franklin *and the* Wharf

Nathaniel Hawthorne

In the year 1716, or about that time, a boy used to be seen on the streets of Boston who was known among his companions as Ben Franklin.

Ben was now about ten years old. He was a bright boy at his books and even a brighter one when at play with his friends. There was something about the lad that always seemed to make him the leader of his companions.

I might tell you many amusing stories about him. No doubt you have read the famous story of Ben and his whistle, and how he gave a whole pocketful of pennies for one. Afterward he found that he had paid too much for his whistle and was very sorry for his bargain.

But Ben had grown to be a large boy since those days and had become much wiser. His mistakes always taught him some valuable lesson.

---

wharf—*pier; dock*   amusing—*funny*

Ben was now at work in his father's shop, and busy as his life was, he still found time for outdoor sports. Ben and his companions were very fond of fishing, and they spent many hours at a pond near the outskirts of the town.

The place where they fished was a marshy spot where sea gulls flitted overhead and marsh grass grew under foot. On the edge of the water there was a bed of wet clay in which the boys were forced to stand while they caught their fish. Here they dabbled in mud like a flock of ducks.

"This is very uncomfortable," said Ben Franklin one day to his friends.

"So it is," said the other boys. "What a pity we have no better place to stand!"

If it had not been for Ben, nothing more would have been done or said about the matter. But it was not in his nature to endure a hardship without trying to find a remedy for it.

"Boys," said Ben, as they were all walking home, "I have thought of a plan which will be for our benefit, and for the public benefit."

His companions were always ready to listen to anything Ben might propose. They remembered how he had sailed across the mill pond by

---

outskirts—*part of a town farthest from the center*

benefit—*advantage; help*
propose—*suggest; recommend*

holding onto his kite string as he lay flat on his back in the water. A boy who could do that might do almost anything.

"What is your plan, Ben? What is it?" they all cried.

They had now come to the spot of ground where a new house was to be built. Scattered about were a great many large stones which were to be used in the building. Ben mounted the highest of these stones so that he might be heard by all.

"I propose, boys," said Benjamin, "that we build a wharf to aid us in our fishing. You see these stones. The workmen plan to use them for the foundation of a house, but that will be for only one man's advantage. My plan is to carry these stones to the edge of the water and build a wharf with them.

"The stones will then be of great help to us and also to the boats passing up and down the stream. You see, the wharf will be of use to many people. The house will benefit only one man. What do you say, boys? Shall we build the wharf?"

"Hurrah! hurrah!" shouted all the boys. "Let's do it at once."

Not one of them asked, "Is it right to build a wharf with stones that belong to another person?" They all agreed to be on the spot that evening and begin their work by moonlight. At the time set, they met and began to remove the heap of stones.

The stones proved heavy and the work harder than they expected. Ben, of course, was the leader, and the boys cheerfully followed his directions. He showed them how to carry the stones, and when they grew tired, he had some joke ready which set them all into a roar of laughter.

After an hour or two of hard work, the stones were carried to the water side, and it was Ben Franklin who planned the building of the wharf. Finally, just as the moon sunk below the horizon, the great work was finished.

"Now, boys," cried Ben, "let's give three cheers and go home to bed. To-morrow we may catch fish at our ease."

"Hurrah! hurrah! hurrah!" shouted the boys.

Then they all went home in such delight that they could hardly get a wink of sleep.

In the morning, when the early sunbeams were gleaming on the steeples and roofs of the town, the masons came to begin work on the new house. But where were their stones? What had become of them?

"The stones must have flown away through the air while we were asleep," said one of the men.

"More likely they were stolen," said another workman.

"But who on earth would think of stealing a heap of stones?" cried a third. "Could a man carry them away in his pocket?"

The master mason said nothing at first. But looking carefully on the ground, he noticed tracks of little feet, some with shoes and some barefoot. He soon saw that the tracks formed a beaten path toward the water's edge.

"Ah, I see what the mischief is," said he, nodding his head. "Those little rascals, the boys, have stolen our stones to build a wharf with."

The masons went to look at the new wharf. And it was well worth looking at, so neatly had it been planned and finished.

---

mason—*a person who works with stone or brick*

"The chaps that built this wharf understood their business," said one of the masons. "I should not be ashamed of such a piece of work myself!"

But the master mason did not enjoy the joke. "The boys must be arrested," he said. "Go call the police."

If the owner of the stolen property had not been more merciful than the master mason, it might have gone hard with Benjamin and his friends. The gentleman had great respect for Ben's father, and he was fond of boys. And so he let them off quite easily.

But the poor boys had to go through another trial, for their fathers soon learned what they had done. Many a rod, I grieve to say, was well worn on that unlucky night. As for Ben, he was less afraid of a whipping than of his father's disapproval.

"Come here, Ben," said his father. "How could you take property which did not belong to you?"

"Why, Father," replied Ben, hanging his head, "if it had been merely for my own benefit I never should have dreamed of it. I thought the wharf would be of use to others, while a house would be of use only to the owner of the stones."

"My son," said Mr. Franklin, "you did very wrong to build a wharf with stones that did not belong to you. There is no more terrible mistake than to think that good will come from a wrong act. Remember, my son, that evil can bring about only evil; good can come only through right doing."

"I will never forget it again," said the lad, bowing his head. And to the close of his life Ben Franklin never forgot this conversation with his father.

Character Theme—Resourcefulness, Integrity, & Wisdom

Thinking It Through

1. Why was fishing from the bank of the pond uncomfortable for Ben and his friends?
2. What bright idea did Ben have as they walked home?
3. Where did the boys get the stones that they used to build their wharf?
4. Why did Ben believe that it was all right to take the stones?
5. What is wrong with Ben's thinking?

THE
Star-Spangled
Banner

Francis Scott Key

Oh say, can you see by the dawn's early light,
    What so proudly we hailed at the twilight's
      last gleaming,
Whose broad stripes and bright stars, through the
      perilous fight
O'er the ramparts we watch'd, were so gallantly
      streaming?
      And the rocket's red glare, the bombs
        bursting in air,
      Gave proof through the night that our flag
        was still there.
    Oh say, does that star-spangled banner yet
      wave
    O'er the land of the free and the home of the
      brave?

hailed—*greeted with enthusiasm*   gallantly—*with boldness*
rampart—*a wall built for defense*

79

On the shore dimly seen through the mists of the
    deep,
    Where the foe's haughty host in dread silence
      reposes,
What is that which the breeze, o'er the towering
    steep,
    As it fitfully blows, half conceals, half
      discloses?
      Now it catches the gleam of the morning's
      first beam,
      In full glory reflected now shines on the
      stream.
   'Tis the star-spangled banner, oh long may it
    wave
   O'er the land of the free and the home of the
    brave.

Oh thus be it ever, when freemen shall stand
    Between their loved homes and war's
      desolation!
Blest with vict'ry and peace, may the heav'n-rescued
    land
    Praise the Power that hath made and
      preserved us a nation!
      Then conquer we must, when our cause it
      is just,
      And this be our motto: "In God is our
      trust,"
    And the star-spangled banner in triumph shall
    wave
    O'er the land of the free and the home of the
    brave.

---

repose—*to rest*

Character Theme—Patriotism

80

A Christmas Gift for the General

Jeannette Covert Nolan

Kennet, at the window, thought that day was
not at all like Christmas. He sighed, yearning in
his heart for other, better years, when the land
was at peace and a holiday could be celebrated
in proper fashion. He wished the Hessian troops
that King George had hired had remained across
the ocean where they belonged and the little town
of Trenton was not hushed, terrified, but a pleasant place in which to live, to make merry with
friends and to share presents and friendly greet-
ings. Today Kennet hadn't offered or received a
single Christmas present—not one!—and this, to
him, seemed tragedy indeed.

He sighed, and Grandfather, hearing the
mourning sound, rose from his fireside chair and

Hessians—*German soldiers hired
by England to fight the Americans*

81

hobbled over to lay a comforting hand on his shoulder.

"What ails you, lad?"

Ah, but Grandfather knew. Grandfather might be old and so crippled now by rheumatism that he must stay always indoors, crouching over the logs to warm his ancient, aching joints; yet his spirit was youthful and strong. In Grandfather's breast burned the pure flame of patriotism. He gripped Kennet's arm and sighed, too.

"Is it true," Kennet asked, turning, "as they are saying: that General Washington must lose the war?"

The old man pursed withered lips. "Lately all reports have been discouraging. The soldiers suffer from dreadful cold, from lack of food and supplies. A dark hour for our country, very dark. But," Grandfather ended bravely, "there's still hope. Maybe in the spring our luck will change."

"You don't mean the Hessians will be quartered here until *spring!*" Kennet wailed. "Oh, but we couldn't bear it. Those harsh, impudent—"

Grandfather lifted a warning finger. "Don't grumble," Grandfather advised.

---

ails—*troubles; bothers*
rheumatism—*a condition causing painful joints and muscles*

impudent—*disrespectful*

But as he hobbled painfully back to his chair, he muttered under his breath that he would give his own life gladly, poor old thing that it was, if only with it he might aid the cause of freedom.

Presently Kennet put on his cap and leather jacket. Carefully, so that Grandfather would not notice, he got a loaf of bread from the cupboard box, a scrap of dried meat from the shelf. He opened the door then and slipped out.

On the porch's narrow step was Toby, the black hound. At sight of his master, the big fellow reared up on hind legs, barked joyously, and began the comical dance which Kennet had taught him.

"No, Toby," Kennet said gravely. "This isn't the time for tricks."

At the boy's command, Toby dropped down obediently on four feet again, wagging his tail.

The dog beside him, Kennet walked to the river and stood for a moment staring out over the ice-choked water. On the far shore, dim behind curtains of falling snow, were the rolling Pennsylvania hills. Nearer, on the Jersey side, were the piers and docks, deserted and idle.

Kennet turned his back on the town. He sought a path at the water's edge. For almost a mile he trudged, winding with the river through thickets of rustling, bare-branched trees and snow-shrouded bushes, reaching at last a clearing where nestled a sturdy wooden shed with peaked roof and little windows.

Over the door was a sign. Kennet read it sorrowfully: "K. Strawn & Son, Carpenters." "K. Strawn?"—that was his Grandfather, so ill and feeble. "Son"—that was Father, dear Father, far from home now, serving in the Continental Army. And there was no carpentry work done here these days.

Yet the shed did hold treasure even now, and Kennet must come occasionally like this to visit it. The shed housed his boat, the roomy, iron-keeled craft which Grandfather and Father had built for him two years ago. *The Madcap*—that was her splendid name, lettered on her stern with yellow paint; and many a fine trip up and down the Delaware had Kennet taken in her. But that, of course, was before the war. Now *The Madcap* was propped, high and dry, on blocks within the shed walls. He didn't know when she would be sailed again.

He unlocked the door and swung it on its rusty hinges. The interior of the shed was gloomy with shadows, chill and bleak. He lighted a candle; his breath formed a little steamy cloud above the orange flame. He set the candle on a chest and bent over

---

snow-shrouded—*covered by snow*

his boat. With a cloth he brushed dust from the seats and polished the metal strips on the rudder. But all this he did absently. Really, he was listening, waiting; and soon he heard what he listened for—a faint yet distinct scratching on the windowpane.

A signal.

Kennet strode to the door, pushed it cautiously open. A man entered. It was the ragged stranger, the wanderer Kennet had met yesterday in the woods, who was so hollow-eyed, starved and mysterious. In the circle of candlelight, the man and the boy faced each other. The man was first to speak.

"So, you came!" His voice was deep and musical. "I was afraid you'd forget."

"No, I couldn't forget my solemn promise."

"And did you bring me food?"

"A snack." Kennet drew the bread and meat from his pocket. "We had nothing else."

"Excellent, my boy!" The man's eyes gleamed. "A feast!" Throwing himself on a bench, he ate ravenously.

Watching, Kennet realized how hungry this stranger must be, and wondered how many hours had passed since his last meal. A great many, probably.

---

ravenously—*greedily; very eagerly*

"As delicious a dinner as I ever had," he said, stooping to caress Toby, to stroke the long velvety ears. "I thank you for your kindness."

Kennet nodded courteously. "You are welcome."

"Sit down." As the boy took a place on the bench, the man said, "Why have you befriended me? You don't know me, never laid eyes on me until twenty-four hours ago."

"It's Christmas," Kennet answered simply.

"And you observe the day with charity?"

"Yes. I know you are deserving. You are not a tramp—even though your clothes are so torn and dirty."

"My clothes *are* shabby, aren't they?" He flipped the sleeve of his threadbare coat. "But they'll do. I don't go about much in society. You didn't mention to anyone that you saw me?" He paused anxiously.

"Not even to my grandfather."

"Good! It's absolutely necessary that I keep undercover. Much depends on it."

Kennet leaned forward. "I think," he said, "you are a soldier."

"A soldier?" The man flushed. "Now why should you think—"

"My father is a soldier, and if he is hungry

today, I should like to believe that someone, somewhere, is feeding—"

But here Kennet paused, for the man was frowning, putting an admonishing finger to his lips. What was that noise at the door? Why did Toby bristle and growl?

The noise again. A stamping of feet, an angry shouting. "Open! Open, in the King's name!"

The King's name? An enemy, then? A Hessian? Kennet tiptoed to the window. Yes, outside in the snow stood a Hessian, uniformed and armed.

"Open!" With his sword, the Hessian pounded the shed door.

Kennet's breath fluttered in his throat. "What shall we do?" he whispered.

"Open, and say you are alone." Swift as lightning, the ragged stranger leaped in *The Madcap*, flung himself down, and crawled under a strip of canvas. He was hidden; he would not be seen.

Slowly Kennet went to the door and unlocked it; he was almost thrown over backward by the violence of the Hessian's rushing entrance. He braced himself before the rude intruder; he waited.

---

admonishing—*warning*

"What are you doing here? Who are you?"

"Kennet Strawn. I live in Trenton with my grandfather. This is his shop."

With the toe of his shiny boot, the Hessian indicated crumbs which had fallen to the floor. "Someone has dined here."

"I carried a bit of lunch in my pocket."

The Hessian lunged and grasped the boy by the shoulder, shaking him fiercely. "You lie! You're sheltering a spy. You'll pay dear for this!"

At that very instant, Toby decided to have a part in the scene. Toby had been snarling, barking. Now, jaws wide, he dashed at the ruffian who threatened his beloved master. The dog's sharp teeth caught the man's leg above the heavy boot, sank in through cloth, found the flesh.

ruffian—*violent, lawless person*

With oaths and a howl of rage and pain, the Hessian released Kennet.

"You beast!" He kicked. He struck out with his fist. He whipped the sword from his belt. The terrible, glistening blade swept upward—

"Oh, please!" Kennet moaned. "Please, don't kill Toby!"

It happened so quickly, the agile leap of the ragged stranger from his canvas cover, the Hessian's astonished outcry. And then they were lurching, tumbling, all over the room, in and out of shadow, the two big men, while Kennet gasped and Toby barked wildly.

The Hessian, after his first surprise, fought like a tiger. At last he yielded.

"Quick!" the stranger muttered. "A rope. A rope."

Kennet fumbled in a chest; dragged forth a length of stout rope. They bound the Hessian with it; they rolled him into a corner.

"Now I must be off!" The stranger was mopping at his forehead, which was grimy and streaked with blood. "Not a minute to lose now!"

Kennet stepped back to view the limp figure of the enemy. "He isn't—isn't dead, is he?"

agile—*quick and easy of movement*

"No. He's not badly hurt. But he'll be quiet for a few hours. Then he'll rouse and spread the alarm. You must go home to your grandfather—and I must get away."

"Why did you jump up? He'd never have noticed you."

"Lie there like a stick of wood and let him mistreat you and kill your dog? Oh, no! No, my friend." He patted Toby's sleek head. "I must get away," he repeated and, his frown deepening, he pointed to *The Madcap*. "Whose boat is this?"

"Boat!" Kennet was startled at the change of subject. "Why—why she's mine."

"Yours, eh? Want to sell her? I've got to have this boat."

Kennet swallowed a huge lump in his throat. "Take the boat. I'll give her to you—for Christmas." Hadn't he been wishing all day for the opportunity to give a Christmas present?

The man bowed. "You'll never regret your generosity. You'll help me move her?"

They worked then like beavers, knocking the blocks from under *The Madcap,* straining every muscle to get her out of the shed, down the slope to the river. Once Kennet, pausing, remarked breathily that the river was full of floating ice and scarcely navigable; escape would be easier by way of the woods. But the stranger only laughed; he said he needed a boat, *this* boat—and he didn't mind ice.

"Good-by, my lad. God bless you."

"Good-by," Kennet quavered. "Can't—can't you tell me *anything* about yourself?"

The stranger was standing in the boat; he looked erect, soldierly. "I'll tell you this; you think you've given me a Christmas token—really, it's for someone else. For a great man, the greatest in the world today, a man who guides your fate, and mine, and all America's. This Christmas present will be delivered to him!" He smiled into the boy's puzzled face. "Hurry home. Be silent about our adventure—and don't be amazed at anything you hear!"

Early on the morning of December twenty-sixth, 1776, while the Hessian troops in Trenton dozed after their drinking and hilarious celebration of the night before, General George Washington and his men advanced upon the town. They entered by two roads, overwhelming and seizing the garrison. For hours the streets echoed with the roar of musket and cannon—and then the Hessians surrendered.

Grandfather, huddled close to the fire, was

---

erect—*upright; straight up*   garrison—*troops stationed in a fort*

91

trying to piece together shreds of rumor and gossip into a logical story.

"They say he came across the Delaware, a few boats pushing through the ice. They say a spy has been here in the neighborhood for several days, obtaining boats by one means or another; and some of 'em splintered and crashed in midstream— and some crossed in safety."

Kennet was kneeling to mend the logs, shielding his face with his palm. *The Madcap,* had she made the crossing safely? Oh, he hoped so! And what if General Washington had been *The Madcap's* passenger—that great man, the greatest in the world, riding to victory in Kennet Strawn's bonny boat!

"The spy, Grandfather? Was he—taken?"

"They say not. They say he's one of the General's trusted officers. A gentleman. A hero." Grandfather fondled Toby's velvet ears. "Now the tide has turned. God is with us and we will win. Freedom will come; it's on the way, in the air." He smiled happily. "Now I am content to die."

But Kennet did not want to die. No, no! This morning, as never before, he wanted to live—for his country.

Character Theme—Courage, Sacrifice, & Patriotism

---

logical—*reasonable*
bonny—*fine; handsome or pretty*

Thinking It Through

1. What war was going on when this story took place?

2. Why was Kennet unhappy at this particular Christmas season?

3. Who were the Hessian troops?

4. What did Kennet bring to the stranger he had met yesterday in the woods?

5. What did the Hessian accuse Kennet of doing?

6. Why did the stranger come out of hiding?

7. What did Kennet give the stranger?

8. Why do you think the story is called, "A Christmas Gift for the General"?

George Washington

Aileen Fisher

There was a lad of long ago
Who yearned to try his luck at sea.
He packed his trunk expectantly
But heard his mother pleading, "No."
    The lad was silent with distress
    Yet did not sit around and pine.
    He learned to run a survey line
    And map the sea of wilderness.
With eyes as steady as the sun
He faced the test and did not run—
That lad whose name was Washington!

There was a man of long ago
Who thought a planter's life was best.
He tilled the land and little guessed
He soon would hear another "No."
    His country gave a call to war!
    He left Mount Vernon's charm and cheer
    And led the army year by year
    Till peace had drowned the cannon's roar.
He heard the call and did not shun
The task ahead that must be done—
That man whose name was Washington!

---

shun—*avoid; to keep
away from*

94

There was a hero long ago
Who thought, "Now I can farm at last.
The war is won, the danger past."
Yet once again the word was "No."
    "We need you, Sir, as President,"
    The letters said that swelled his mail.
    "Your country calls; you must not fail.
    We need you, Sir!" And so he went.
He left no call, no task undone
But met each test and always won—
That man whose name was Washington!

Character Theme—Helpfulness &
            Service

DANIEL BOONE'S DAUGHTER

Aileen Fisher

The five Indians hurried their captives along the narrow forest trail. Only one of the five could speak any English. "Walk fast," he told the three frightened girls. "Walk fast. No make trouble."

Jemima Boone blinked back her tears, trying not to cry. But with every step, they were getting farther away from the safety of the little log cabins at Fort Boonesborough, farther away from rescue.

Jemima wondered if anyone back at the fort had missed them yet. Had they guessed what had happened?

A choking sob drifted back to Jemima from her best friend, Frances Calloway. For all her bragging earlier that afternoon, Frances was scared to pieces, now. And Betsy Calloway was scared, too, even though she was much older than Frances and Jemima.

Betsy was sixteen, already. She should have known better. Yet she was the one who'd suggested the whole thing. "Let's take the canoe and paddle

---

Boonesborough (bo͞onz′bər·ō)

up around the bend," she'd said. Since Betsy knew a lot about handling a canoe, Jemima and Frances hadn't hesitated.

No, Jemima had not hesitated. But in her heart, she was sure that her father would have said, "You stay at the fort, Jemima. The river's no place for girls."

Jemima sighed, now. Her legs were becoming tired from hurrying so, and her heart was aching from fear and regret. If only they'd been satisfied with a brief paddle in the canoe! If only they'd had sense enough to turn back before ending up in trouble!

But once Frances had seen those pretty flowers growing on the north bank, there was no way to talk her out of picking them.

All Jemima's objections had been brushed off. "There may be Indians on the north bank!" she had said.

"Silly," Betsy had replied. "Indians so close to the fort? We haven't seen any Indians around the fort for months and months!"

And then Frances had said, "I'm surprised at you, Jemima. Imagine Daniel Boone's daughter being such a scared-y-cat!"

But now Jemima was sorry that she had let Frances and Betsy talk her into doing what she knew was wrong.

If there was one thing she had learned from her father, it was a healthy respect for the Indians.

Daniel Boone knew the Indians hated the white settlers because, as they moved West, they kept pushing the Indians from their own hunting grounds. And his understanding of the Indians made him realize how dangerous they could be, so he never took chances with them.

He had warned Jemima not to take chances, either. But steering their canoe close to the north bank to pick flowers this afternoon had been taking a chance. Suddenly they had discovered that they were stuck on a sand bar, just off shore.

And before they could push their canoe

loose, hands
had reached out
from behind the
canebrake on the
shore to seize them.
They were Indian
hands, Shawnee hands,
the same hands that were
urging them along the trail
now, farther and farther from
Fort Boonesborough.

Each weary mile that they
walked took them deeper into Indian
Country. And Jemima realized that if the
Shawnees once got them beyond the Ohio River,
even her father would not be able to find them.

Jemima quivered with fear as she thought
about it. But this was no time to be afraid. She
must keep her eyes open every moment, and not
miss a chance to outsmart the Indians.

canebrake—*a thick growth of cane plants*
Shawnee (shô·nē′)

"Walk fast," growled the Indian behind her.
Then, as if he were reading her thoughts, he
added, "No trouble."

Jemima knew what he meant by "no trouble."
He meant not to leave any signs that would show
a rescue party which way they had come.

But that kind of "trouble" was the only hope
for Jemima and her friends. And she was delighted, a moment later, to notice a fat brown mushroom at the side of the trail up ahead. If only she
could kick off one corner of it.

She stared up at the trees as she walked, so
the Indians wouldn't guess what she had in mind.
A piece of mushroom would be a perfect trail
marker for her father and the rescue party!

The thought of her father gave Jemima new
courage. In a low, firm voice, she said to Frances, who was still sobbing, "Don't be so worried,
Frances. My father will be able to find us, no
matter how far we go."

"But how can he?" Frances choked. "We've
been crossing and recrossing our tracks in the
canebrake. And then they made us wade up that
creek a long way . . ."

"He will find us," insisted Jemima. And she
herself was surprised at how convincing her voice
sounded. Listening to her own words seemed to

strengthen her belief in what she was saying. "Don't worry, Frances," she repeated. "He'll find us, all right."

"Stop talk," the Indian demanded, moving closer. "No talk. Understand?"

Jemima sighed. Maybe he could make her stop talking, but he could not make her stop trying to leave a trail. As she walked along, Jemima secretly worked loose a long blue thread from her dress, and dropped it behind her on a bush.

It was getting darker in the woods now. And she was glad of that.

Jemima knew it was not too dark for the Indians to follow their own forest trails. But she knew it was too dark for them to watch every movement of her hands and feet. An overturned stone, torn threads from her clothing, a broken twig—these would make the trail an open book for Daniel Boone to read.

The Indians hurried their captives along at a dogtrot. At an open place on a high bank above the creek, the spokesman said, "We stop. Too dark."

The Indians tied the girls to some trees at the edge of the clearing. Then they took out their food pouches. They built no campfire.

---

dogtrot—*a fast, steady walk*

Indians and captives alike received their share of the dried corn and dried meat that the Indians had brought with them.

"Sun-up, we go," said the Indian. "Now, all sleep."

Leaning up against the tree trunk, Jemima stretched out her tired legs and did her best to comfort Frances and Betsy.

"They'll find us tomorrow," Jemima whispered bravely.

"How?" groaned Frances. "We had a three or four-hour start, maybe more."

"My father will find us," Jemima whispered back. "I'm *sure* he will."

"How will he know which way to go?"

"He'll find our trail, somehow," replied Jemima. "You'll see. Don't worry. Now let's try to get some sleep."

Next day the Indians drove the girls along even harder. They made them backtrack and follow stream beds, keeping a constant watch on all of them. Once when Jemima "stumbled" on a root, displacing a stone, they carefully put it back in place and covered all signs of the fall.

Still, Jemima managed to drop bits of cloth and pieces of thread here and there.

But they were getting nearer and nearer to

the Ohio River, farther and farther from Fort Boonesborough! Jemima decided to try something else to gain time.

She pretended to start crying. As soon as the Indian was within hearing distance, she sobbed loudly, "Father won't *ever* be able to find us! He's probably still wandering back in that first canebrake."

The Indian laughed. "No find, huh?" He spoke to the other Shawnees. They laughed, too. "Too bad. No find."

Jemima flung herself upon the ground, still putting on a great show of tears. "I'm so tired, I can't walk another step. I can't! I can't!"

"Anything to gain time," she said to Frances under her breath.

"It won't do any good," groaned Frances. "They won't find us, no matter how much time you gain!"

But after that, the Indians did not make their three captives go along so fast. They seemed to be convinced that no one, not even Daniel Boone, could follow the trail.

Noticing that the Indians were not watching them quite so closely, Jemima left more and more markers on the trail.

Toward evening, one of the men shot a deer, and they made a fire to cook it. The girls, tied to trees nearby, watched anxiously.

The Indians were working busily near the campfire when, suddenly, shots rang out.

Jemima screamed, "Father! Father!" And Frances started to cry, but not from fear this time. As the Indians leaped for the safety of the woods, Daniel Boone stepped from behind a tree, his gun smoking. Mr. Calloway and the rest of the rescue party followed him.

Jemima felt her father's strong arms hugging her tight. Then he untied the strips of deerskin which held her to the tree. "My poor little girl," he said. "You must have been scared!"

"I was at first," Jemima said. "But, you know, Father, when I saw how scared Frances was, everything changed. The more I tried to make her feel better, the better I felt myself. It was as if my little bit of courage just kept growing and grow- ing!"

"That's the way it is with courage," Daniel Boone said, "only not everybody finds that out." He studied his daughter seriously for a moment. Then his eyes began to twinkle.

"Speaking of finding things out, I've been wondering about something. Which one of you girls managed to break off the edge of that mushroom?"

Character Theme—Courage & Resourcefulness

Thinking It Through

1. Where did the girls in this story live?
2. Why had they gone so far from the fort?
3. Did Jemima think it was a good idea to pick flowers? Why?
4. Who had captured the girls?
5. Why was Jemima trying to leave trail markers behind them?
6. What truth did Jemima learn about courage from this experience?

A Present for a President

Janet P. Shaw

"Ah-choo! Ah-choo! Ah-choo!" sneezed Sally
Ann Everett, wakening herself out of a sound
sleep. Something soft and fuzzy was rubbing the
end of her nose and would not be brushed away.

"Please go 'way, Jerry. It isn't time to get up yet;
it's dark," she said sleepily, thinking that her younger
brother, Jerry, was up to his usual tricks. But this
Jerry did not "go 'way," and the fuzzy something
nestled still more closely to her cheek and tickled her
nose saucily until she was wide awake.

Then Sally Ann remembered. She laughed
quietly to herself in the darkness as she reached
under the covers and drew out a pair of very large,
beautiful, white wool socks! She had made them
for a birthday present for her dear friend, Abra-
ham Lincoln, and had finished them only the day
before. She had been so proud of her work that
she had taken the socks to bed with her and then
had forgotten all about them!

Sally Ann had never given Mr. Lincoln a

present before, although she lived in southern Indiana not far from his old home, and had known and loved him all her life. This was partly because she had never had anything all her own to give him. This year, however, she had her pet sheep, Susie, and Susie's wool made beautiful yarn for knitting socks.

Sally Ann had taken care of Susie ever since her father had brought in the poor little half-frozen lamb he had found lost in the woods one cold winter night, and had given it to her to nurse back to life. At first Susie had slept in a basket beside Sally Ann's bed and had lived on warm milk like other babies. And now that she was a grown-up sheep with a lamb of her own, she still stayed in the front yard under her mistress's window most of the time, and she brought her lamb to the door every morning and waited until Sally Ann cleaned and brushed their thick coats. Their wool was almost as soft and white as swan's-down, and, if you had happened to see them grazing at a distance, you might have thought that two little fleecy summer clouds had got lost from the sky and had floated down to the Everett's yard to rest awhile.

All Sally Ann's friends were knitting for the soldiers, for the war had begun not long before

---

fleecy—*like fleece; light*

and most of the fathers and big brothers of the neighborhood had enlisted in order to help Mr. Lincoln. But no one made such beautiful socks as those Sally Ann knitted from Susie's wool. So many people had admired them and said they were "fit for a king" that Sally Ann finally decided that maybe they were fit for her own President to wear.

The very next day she went up to the attic where the choicest wool was stored and brought a great white bundle, almost as big as she could carry. This she carded and spun into yarn on her own little spinning wheel, and then she knitted the socks as neatly as she could.

Now the question was how to get them to Washington in time for Mr. Lincoln's birthday on the twelfth of February, only two weeks away. She knew the mails were not safe in wartime, and that sometimes you had to wait weeks and weeks to find a traveler who could carry a package east. And, of course, a birthday present wouldn't be exactly a birthday gift unless it reached Mr. Lincoln on the right day.

Sally Ann lay quietly in her little white bed thinking about this question and wondering what to do. As she couldn't decide the matter, she was just about to doze off for another nap, when, all of a sudden, something went, "tick-tack, tick-tack,"

on the dark
window
near her bed.
And when she
went to see what
the matter was
there was her own
dear soldier father,
standing in the yard
below—the very best
messenger she could
ask for!

"Is that you, Captain Daddy?" she called softly as she raised the window.

"Yes, daughter," he answered in a low tone of voice. "I have two tired men with me, and we need food and a few hours' rest before we go on to Washington with important news for the President. The enemy have given us a merry chase, and they may be on our heels at any minute. Waken your mother and Jerry, but tell them to be very quiet."

"Of course," whispered Sally Ann as she slipped on her wrapper and hurried downstairs.

Mrs. Everett was used to preparing meals at a moment's notice, for Captain Everett was one of President Lincoln's trusted officers, and he often sent him to secure important facts about the movements of the enemy, and the Captain always stopped at his home when he was in that part of the country. So, by the time the men had cared for their tired horses, she had bowls of smoking hot soup on the table and was busy making man-sized sandwiches of flaky homemade bread and delicious baked ham and roast beef, while Sally Ann and Jerry brought plates heaped high with doughnuts and cookies and explored the cellar for spicy apple butter, and preserves, and other good things which were stored there.

Then, when the soldiers had satisfied their hunger and had gone up to a hidden room in the attic to rest, Mrs. Everett and the children spent a busy hour doing all they could for the comfort of

---

wrapper—*a loose garment that wraps around the body*   cellar—*room or rooms below ground level in a building*

the men. They brushed and cleaned the travel-worn suits and boots, placed clean underwear near the beds, and, when it was almost time to waken the travelers, they filled the knapsacks with bottles of hot coffee and packages of food for the long journey.

All this time Sally hadn't given one thought to her precious birthday present for Mr. Lincoln! But finally, when the horses were at the door and the men were about to leave, she suddenly remembered and ran to get it. She was just about to show it to her father and ask him to take it to Mr. Lincoln when she heard her mother say to him, "John, why don't you take the children with you until you reach the highway? They know the shortcut through the woods better than you do, and they can find more hiding places than the squirrels themselves. If they meet the soldiers, they can explain that old Bess, our cow, has been ailing for several days and I have sent them to ask Mr. Moll, the driver of the stagecoach on that road, to come over and doctor her. He knows a great deal about caring for sick animals."

"I'd certainly like a little longer visit with my son and daughter, if it will be safe," said Captain Everett, and when he had thought the matter over

---

knapsack—*a leather or canvas bag for carrying things*

for a minute, he called, "Get some warm wraps, children, and ride through the woods with us if you want to. Jerry, you may ride ahead with one of the men and show us the way and, Sally, you may hop up in front of me in your old place."

You may be sure that this plan suited the children exactly. A moment later the little company set out in the cold, gray light of the winter morning. Jerry looked as much like his father as he could, in his big blue overcoat and cap like those the soldiers wore. Sally Ann, in her pretty red hood and cape trimmed with soft rabbit's fur, snuggled close in her father's arms. As they rode along, Sally Ann took out the precious present and asked her father rather anxiously whether he thought Mr. Lincoln would like the socks.

"I'm sure he will," answered Captain Everett, when he had looked at them admiringly. "No one could ask for more beautiful knitting," he said, "and I know Mr. Lincoln will feel honored to receive a present from such a loyal little girl as my Sally Ann. You know he has often said that he has always regretted the fact that his girls are all boys."

"He told me that, too," laughed Sally Ann.

They chatted happily together in this way until they were almost through the woods. But just as Sally Ann and Jerry were about to say good-bye and turn back home, suddenly they heard men's voices and the sound of horses trotting on the frozen road not many rods away, though still hidden from sight by the bushes.

"Enemy soldiers looking for you!" whispered Sally Ann with tears in her eyes.

"Confederates," agreed her father. "I thought we'd thrown those men off the track at last. They've followed us for a week. Don't be afraid; we're not caught yet," he added, as he lifted her to the ground.

No one knew what to do for a minute, but Captain Everett soon took command. "We'll have to separate," he decided. "Jameson, you and Clark take the horses back to the thicket we just passed, and if we are discovered, make for the other road as fast as you can. The children will wait for the stage driver, as their mother planned. Perhaps they can keep the men from turning through the woods and finding our tracks. I'll stay some place nearby to protect them if necessary."

"This big fallen tree trunk will make a fine hiding place for you," suggested Sally Ann. "We often hide there. It's hollow from end to end. You creep inside and I'll sit on the end nearest the road so that no one will suspect that anyone is inside.

rod—*a measure of length; 16½ ft.*

And here is my present for Mr. Lincoln. If you are in danger, leave the socks behind, if necessary."

"I'll tell the President that you saved me and my men to be his present, dear," whispered back her father affectionately from the depths of the hollow tree.

A moment later when the soldiers came in sight, they found no one about but a rather sleepy appearing boy, who said he was waiting for the driver of the stagecoach to get him to doctor a sick cow, and his pretty sister perched on a fallen tree trunk close by.

Sally Ann looked so sweet and dainty in her red coat and hood that the captain of the company, who had a little girl of his own at home, walked over to chat with her for a few minutes and sat down beside her on the log!

"Oh, dear," said Sally Ann to herself, "what shall I do?" But she knew she mustn't let the

---

affectionately—*in a tender, loving way*

man know she was worried, so she chatted along as entertainingly as she could.

"We're looking for the home of a man named Captain Everett," the stranger said at last, as he rose to leave. "Can you direct us to the place?"

"Oh, yes, indeed," answered Sally Ann—and then told him how to reach the house by the very longest way. "You'll have to ride back a mile or more to the crossroads and then go east until you reach the highway; then follow that until you reach a white house with green blinds."

"And where will Everett and his men be by that time?" exclaimed the captain as he hurried back to his men. "They've given us the slip a dozen times during the last few days. I think their leader's name ought to be 'Captain Fox.'"

Sally Ann thought she heard a little chuckle over this remark down deep in the hollow log, but she could not be sure. As the captain and his men rode off a few minutes later, it is certain that he did not hear it nor suspect for a minute that the log on which he had been sitting housed her two precious presents for President Lincoln.

"Captain Fox" got away safely once more, and not long after a precious letter came to the Everett home, addressed to "Miss Sally Ann Everett" and postmarked, "From the White House, Washington." In it Mr. Lincoln thanked her warmly for both the birthday presents she had sent him and praised her for the quick wit which had helped to save the lives of his soldiers. Then he added, "I shall take great pleasure in wearing your beautiful gift. While the handsome garments comfort my body, they will also warm my heart, for they will remind me of the enduring affection and sympathy of my old friends in southern Indiana. And, as I have often said, there are no better people to be found in these United States."

Sally Ann carried this beautiful letter with her for years and years, until it fell to pieces, literally worn-out. But the affection of Lincoln for his old friends never wore out, and today, if you will visit the places where he once lived, you will find in many homes, memories of the great man as interesting as this story of the present which Sally Ann sent to her beloved President.

Character Theme—Courage & Resourcefulness

Thinking It Through

1. What President did Sally Ann want to give her gift to?

2. What gift did Sally Ann make for the President?

3. Who were Sally Ann's father and his men hiding from?

4. Where did Sally Ann tell her father to hide when they heard the Confederate soldiers?

5. When the Confederate soldiers asked directions to Captain Everett's house, what did Sally Ann tell them?

6. Why does the story say that Sally Ann gave two presents to the President?

John Paton

Hugh T. Kerr

Boy with a Purpose

John Paton was born in a poor but very happy home in Scotland. His parents often prayed that their eleven children would grow into good, useful adults.

Once when John's father was away in another town working, there was nothing to eat in the home. John's mother had to coax the children off to bed hungry and unfed.

The next day, a visitor came to the door. He had brought flour, potatoes, and cheese for them!

Mrs. Paton gathered her children around her. "Oh my children," she said, "love your Heavenly Father. Tell Him in faith and prayer all your needs, and He will supply your wants so far as it shall be for your good and His glory." You do not wonder that the children all grew up to be good men and women.

John, the oldest, however, became not only good but great. There are no books in the world as interesting and thrilling as the story of his life. He was a missionary for many years in the South Sea Islands, and the change brought about by his work there reads like one of the Bible stories of the New Testament.

When he was a boy, John longed to study. His parents were too poor to pay for his education, however, and he had to work. Once he saved enough to go to school for six weeks, and they were precious weeks for him. Then he had to return to work and could study only at night and on rainy days.

He found work with a company of government engineers who were testing the land near his home. He walked four miles every morning and evening to and from his work, using his evenings for study. When lunch time came, instead of playing soccer and other games like the rest of the boys, he found a quiet corner on the riverbank and worked away at his books.

He did not know he was being watched, but his employer's home was on the other side of the river, and this man became much interested in the lad who was so fond of books and study.

South Sea Islands—*islands in the South Pacific Ocean*

employer—*person or company for whom one works*

One day, John's master called him to his office and asked him what he was studying. John was surprised but told him the whole truth. The man was very interested, and the next day he told John he would send him to school and pay all his expenses if he would sign an agreement to remain with him for seven years. This was a fine chance for a poor boy! Why, even rich boys would gladly have accepted it. But John Paton had other plans. He politely refused and thanked the man for his kindness.

The man was surprised and a little angry. "Why will you not accept such a good offer?" he asked John.

"Because," said the lad, "my life is given to another Master, and so I cannot promise to work for you for seven years."

"To whom?" said the man bluntly.

The boy, unafraid, replied, "To the Lord Jesus. I want to prepare as soon as possible for His service in preaching the gospel."

The man was very angry and said in a loud voice, "Accept my offer, or you are fired on the spot."

And fired he was, for John would not change his mind. John told the man that if he accepted the position he would have to give up his hope of becoming a minister, and he would not do that. After thanking the man for his good intentions, he received his pay. Then he packed up all his belongings and went back home, sad and heavy of heart.

He had no work and not enough money to pay for his schooling. It looked as if he had come to an iron gate and found it closed in his face.

But when he came closer, he found that the gate stood open, for some of his friends heard what had happened and how brave and good he had been. They offered him other work, and in the fall he began to work with a church in the big city of Glasgow. He visited the poor of Glasgow for this church and also went to college.

In time he finished his studies and became a minister. He went far away as a missionary, and when he returned home, thousands went to hear him tell about his work among the cannibals in the South Sea Islands.

Dr. Paton lived and worked in the South Sea Islands for fifty years, and thousands of the islanders became Christians and were his loyal and true friends.

Every young person ought to have a purpose in life. God has a plan for each of us. We need to discover that plan and fulfill it.

Glasgow (glăs′kō)—*a large city in Scotland*

Dare to be a Daniel,
Dare to stand alone,
Dare to have a purpose true
And dare to make it known.

Character Theme—Faith & Purpose

Thinking It Through

1. Who did Mrs. Paton teach her children to love and trust?

2. What was John Paton not allowed to do very often because the family was poor?

3. Why was John's employer interested in him?

4. What unusual offer did his employer give him?

5. When John turned down his employer's offer, what did his employer do?

6. What job did John get instead?

7. Later, what did John Paton do?

From the Bible

But Daniel purposed in his heart that he would not defile himself with the portion of the king's meat, nor with the wine which he drank. . . .   —*Daniel 1:8*

The Wonderful Well

Hugh T. Kerr

Aniwa is the name of the little island in the
South Pacific Ocean where John G. Paton lived
for many years. It is less than nine miles long
and three and a half miles wide. The sea breaks
heavily, with thundering roar, and the white surf
rolls in, furious and far. But there are days of
calm, when all the sea is glass, and the spray on
the reef is only a fringe of silver.

There was one thing about this beautiful
island which made it not a very pleasant place for
a missionary to live. There was no good water
on the island, and nobody can get along without
water. "How did the natives live there then?" you
ask. Well, they gathered the rain when it fell, and
they drank the dirty water that remained in the
swamps; but the best water they had was in the
coconut. They would break the nut and drink

Aniwa (än′ē·wä)
reef—*a ridge of rock or coral
lying at or near the surface of the water*

fringe—*a border or outer edge*

the milklike water inside it. They also had sugar cane, and would chew it when they were thirsty instead of seeking a drink of water.

Dr. Paton was not used to living without fresh, clean water, however, and decided to dig a well. The people had never heard of such a thing.

When the missionary told the old chief that he was going to sink a deep well into the earth to see if God would send up water from below, the old chief looked at him in surprise. "O Missi," he cried, "your head is going wrong; you are losing something, or you would not talk like that. Don't let our people hear you talking like that, or they will never listen to your word or believe you again."

But the well was started, and the natives gathered around to see the missionary digging into the earth to find rain. They all thought he had lost his mind and was crazy.

Dr. Paton was not very strong, and he grew weary and tired, and so he planned to get the natives to help him. This is how he did it. He brought a box of fish hooks from his home and showed them to the people. He said, "I will give one of them to every man who fills and turns over three buckets of dirt out of this hole." They all wanted to take their turn, and soon the well was twelve feet deep.

One morning when they came to begin work, the sides had fallen in, and the work had to be begun over again. And what was worse, the natives were now so frightened that they would have nothing to do with it.

The old chief, whose name was Namakei, begged the missionary to stop. "You only dig your own grave!" Chief Namakei cried. "Rain will never come up from below."

But Dr. Paton was not to be turned from his task. He knew that he needed water, and he also knew that if God would give him fresh water from the earth, the natives would believe His Word and follow Him always. He toiled on alone until the well was thirty feet deep and the earth was becoming moist.

Namakei (näm′ə·kī)

He feared the water might be salty and all his work for nothing, but he worked away. As he worked, the words "living water" kept singing like music in his soul.

One evening he said to the old chief, "I think God will give us water tomorrow from that hole."

The chief said, "No, Missi; you will never see rain coming up from the earth. We expect to see you some day drop through into the sea, and the sharks will eat you."

Next morning the missionary began his work at daybreak and dug a little hole two feet deep in the bottom of the well. Suddenly, the water rushed up and began to fill the hole! Muddy as it was, he tasted it. In his great delight, the cup fell from his hand, and in that muddy well he gave praise to God, Who had answered his prayer. It was water! It was living water!

The people gathered around the well, and the old chief looked at the water in the cup and then touched it to see if it were really water. After tasting it, he shouted, "Rain! Rain! Yes, it is rain! But how did you get it?"

The happy missionary said, "God gave it to me out of your own earth in answer to our labors and our prayers. Go and see it for yourselves."

To them it was a miracle, and they exclaimed,

"Missi, wonderful, wonderful is the work of your Jehovah God! No god of Aniwa ever helped us this way."

And it was a miracle, for all through the years the well gave forth fresh water. Although the natives tried to sink six or seven other wells, they came to either rock or salt water.

But this is not all of the story. The best is yet to tell. Next Sunday, Chief Namakei wanted to preach. The people of the island came to see their chief-turned-missionary and to hear him preach.

It was a great sermon— one of the greatest that was ever preached. Chief Namakei told the people that since Jehovah God had given them rain from the earth, he was ready to give up his heathen idols and believe in the Christian God. "Jehovah God has sent us rain from the earth," he said. "Why should He

heathen—*one who is not a worshiper of the true God*

not also send His Son from Heaven? Namakei stands up for Jehovah."

That afternoon, the chief himself and several of his people brought their idols and cast them down at the feet of the missionary. For days after that, the people kept coming with their idols and giving them up, saying, "Jehovah! Jehovah!" The idols of wood were burned in the fire, and those that would not burn were buried in the ground. Aniwa became a Christian island where one could hear the sound of the church bells and where there were no longer any idols or any heathen.

That is the wonderful story of the wonderful well, and it preaches to us as it preached to the people of Aniwa long, long ago. And this is the sermon it preaches:

> Faith in God is never really disappointed. All the treasures of Heaven and earth are His, and those who seek Him find Him.
>
> Faith in God does not excuse any of us from hard work. Dr. Paton prayed long and earnestly, but he worked and toiled as hard as he trusted and prayed. It is an old and a true saying that
>
> > God helps those
> > Who help themselves.

Character Theme—Faith & Perseverance

Thinking It Through

1. What problem did John Paton face on the island of Aniwa?

2. What did John decide to do to solve the problem?

3. What did the natives think when they saw John digging a well?

4. What did the natives call the water that came from the well?

5. After the well was dug, what did Chief Namakei want to do?

6. As a sign that they were giving up their idols to trust in the true God, what did the natives do?

From the Bible

And let us not be weary in well doing: for in due season we shall reap, if we faint not.

—*Galatians 6:9*

Consider
Christina G. Rossetti

Consider
The lilies of the field whose bloom is brief:
    We are as they;
Like them we fade away,
    As doth a leaf.

Consider
The sparrows of the air of small account:
    Our God doth view
Whether they fall or mount,—
    He guards us too.

Consider
The lilies that do neither spin nor toil,
    Yet are most fair:
What profits all this care
    And all this toil?

Consider
The birds that have no barn nor harvest-weeks;
    God gives them food:
Much more our Father seeks
    To do us good.

---

account—*worth, importance*

An Mei Says Thank You

A Story from Hong Kong

Matilda Nordtvedt

An Mei said the words over to herself as she hurried along the crowded Hong Kong street: "In everything give thanks." What did they mean?

Her mind drifted back to the big house where she had gone to sell artificial flowers that afternoon. Sometimes it was frightening going to the big houses where the rich people lived. Often a servant would come out and say, "Of course my mistress doesn't want to buy your flowers," and chase her away. Sometimes a kind servant would come to the door and call the mistress herself to look at An Mei's flowers. At such times, the Chinese girl caught a glimpse of beautiful, large rooms filled with fine furniture.

Today at the big yellow house with the lovely garden in front, An Mei had heard the strange words. A group of children were sitting in the garden repeating them with a kind-looking Chinese woman. "Thank God for everything, boys

---

An Mei (än mā)
artificial—*made by human means; not natural*

and girls," she said. "The true God loves you and has a wonderful plan for you."

When the woman saw An Mei at the gate, she left the children and came toward her.

"Beautiful flowers, very cheap," said An Mei, just as her mother had taught her to say.

The woman hesitated a moment then chose five red roses, took a small purse from her pocket, and handed An Mei some coins. "Never mind the change," she said.

"Thank you! Thank you very much," said An Mei. The woman returned to the children. As An Mei turned to leave, she heard the strange words again: "In everything give thanks."

"I cannot go to school," thought An Mei, "because it costs too much, and besides, I must help Mother earn money for our food. But I can learn something. I will say the words over and over until I will never forget them. Perhaps Mother can tell me what they mean."

An Mei made her way to the large building to meet her mother. She found her sitting on the shelf she rented each day, busily finishing a flower. She looked up briefly when An Mei appeared. Her face became sad. "You didn't sell them all," she said wearily, seeing the flowers An Mei still carried.

An Mei pulled her coins out of her pocket and handed them to her mother. "No, Mother, but one kind lady paid me double for five. We will still have enough for rice tonight."

Mrs. Wang looked at the coins and smiled. "Enough for rice and an egg or two. You are a good girl, An Mei. As soon as I finish this flower, we will go. Someone else will be coming to use the shelf for the night."

"I wish we could," An Mei said.

"It costs more to rent at night," her mother answered as she put the finishing touches on the flower and carefully gathered up her belongings. An Mei carried the sack containing the two kettles they owned, while Mother shouldered the rest of their few possessions. Making their way down the busy street, they stopped to buy rice, a few vegetables, and two eggs. Tonight they would have a feast. An Mei's mouth watered. She was very hungry.

That night, as An Mei lay in the shelter she and her mother had made with sacks and cardboard, she thought of the words she had heard that day: "In everything give thanks." What did they mean? She had meant to ask her mother, but now she was fast asleep on the sacks beside her. "Tomorrow I will find out," An Mei promised herself as she drifted off to sleep.

When An Mei asked the meaning of the words the next morning, her mother gave a short, bitter laugh. "The words are for rich people, An Mei. For what have we to be thankful? We are poor refugees without a home and barely enough to eat." A sigh escaped her lips as she put the leftover rice from last night into two bowls and handed one of them to her daughter. Silently they ate their scanty breakfast.

After they had eaten, they gathered up the sacks and kettles. An Mei helped her mother

---

refugee—*a person who flees his country to live somewhere else because of war or persecution* carry the things to the big house and the rented shelf. Then she took a large bunch of flowers and started off to try to sell them.

"Nobody wants flowers today," An Mei murmured as she went from door to door and was turned away every time. After trudging for hours, she had not sold even one!

An Mei thought of the words she had heard yesterday. Somehow, they seemed like a key that would unlock something strange and wonderful. She must find out what they meant. The big yellow house was not too far away. She would go to see if the children were meeting in the garden again. Perhaps she could hear more of the beautiful words.

An Mei's heart beat fast with excitement when she arrived at the gate of the yellow house. She heard singing from the garden. The children were there again. Forgetting to be afraid, An Mei walked through the trees toward the group of children. When she drew near enough to see them, her mouth dropped open in surprise. They were not rich children, as she had supposed, but poor ones like herself. Some were even wearing rags.

Suddenly shy, An Mei ducked behind a flowering shrub before anyone could see her.

The kind Chinese lady who had paid double for An Mei's flowers the day before began to speak to the children. She told them of a person named Jesus, the Son of God, Who lived in Heaven with His Father, but because the people on earth were poor and miserable, came to earth to help them.

"Jesus loves each one of you very much," she said. "He died to pay for your sins. He died to give you true riches."

Then the children repeated the words they had learned the day before: "In everything give thanks."

"Now let us thank Jesus for the eternal riches He gives," said the woman, "forgiveness, peace, and eternal life. Let us thank Him too for the hard things in our lives, because they make us want the true riches."

An Mei forgot all about selling her flowers. Eagerly she listened. When the prayers were over, the woman said, "Now we will have our reading lesson."

An Mei could remain in hiding no longer. How she wanted to learn to read! Mother had tried to teach her a little in the evenings, but darkness fell so quickly, and they had no light. Besides, they had no books. Mother wrote the words in the dirt, and they were hard to see.

An Mei edged closer to the group, looking hungrily at the books the woman was passing out. Suddenly the woman looked up and saw An Mei.

"Why, here is the flower girl. Would you like to join us?"

An Mei held out her hand for the book, happy beyond words. Eagerly she listened as the teacher explained the words. Oh, what fun! Later the teacher gave her a slate, and she learned to write a few simple Chinese characters. All too soon, the class was over and it was time to leave.

"You may come again tomorrow," said the woman to An Mei as she collected the books and slates. "This is a school for refugee children. It is free."

An Mei was so happy she ran nearly all the way to the big building where her mother was working. Not until she was almost there did she remember the flowers she held tightly in her hand. She had not sold one today! What would Mother say? What would they have to eat?

An Mei's mother was very sad when An Mei told her she had not sold any flowers. "What did you do all day long?" she demanded.

An Mei told her about the school. "Oh, Mother, it was so wonderful! We had a book and a slate, and the teacher said I could come back—"

Mother was angry. "Foolish girl!" she scolded. "You cannot eat books and slates! How can we buy food when you do not work? You may not go back to the school. School is for rich children who do not need to work."

An Mei wanted to tell her mother about the eternal riches the woman had told her about, but she did not dare. Right now, Mother was hungry. An Mei was hungry, too. What good were eternal riches now, when there was no money for food? Wearily she followed her mother down the crowded street. Her stomach hurt because it was so empty.

It was hard for An Mei to fall asleep in their shelter of sacks and cardboard that night. One reason was that her stomach hurt because she had had nothing to eat since early morning. Another reason was that she kept thinking about the wonderful things she had heard that day at the garden school. Could she talk to this Jesus as the other refugee children did?

An Mei remembered the teacher's words: "Thank Jesus for the eternal riches He gives, and thank Him too for the hard things in our lives, because they make us want the true riches."

But how could An Mei thank Jesus that Mother would not let her attend the garden school anymore? She enjoyed it so much!

"In everything give thanks." An Mei did not understand the words, but she decided to try to do as they said, anyway. "Thank You, Jesus, for everything," she whispered. A happy feeling stole into the Chinese girl's heart as she said the words. It was as if she had some of the eternal riches already! At last, she fell asleep.

There was no leftover rice for breakfast. An Mei felt ashamed. "I will work hard today, Mother," she promised.

"We are both too hungry to work hard," Mother said. She sounded weak and tired. Their walk to the rented shelf took longer than usual, because Mother walked so slowly.

An Mei tried to sell her flowers, but without success. "Someone else was just here selling the same thing," said the maid at one of the large houses. "Nobody wants artificial flowers anymore."

An Mei's heart sank. If nobody wanted to buy their flowers, how could they live? How could they eat? Her stomach hurt so much now that it was hard to walk from one house to the other. The school she had gone to yesterday seemed like only a dream now, the beautiful words for somebody else, not her. But she said them anyway, "Thank You, Jesus, for everything," and her heart felt a little lighter.

"I will go to the teacher and tell her I cannot come again," she said when she came to the corner near the big yellow house. "She was so kind." An Mei trudged up to the gate, pushed it open, and walked through the trees to the door.

A young Chinese woman answered the doorbell. She looked cross. "What do you want?" she demanded. "Deliveries are made at the back door."

"I'm not making a delivery," answered An Mei breathlessly. "I want to see—" Suddenly she realized she did not even know the woman's name.

"Mrs. Li? She can't see you now. She is entertaining a group of ladies at tea!"

An Mei did not move. She felt so disappointed that big tears welled in her eyes. She tried hard to keep them back, but they rolled down her cheeks anyway.

The maid looked at her sharply. "Are you one of the refugee children?" she asked, not unkindly.

An Mei nodded.

"School is not until one o'clock. Come back then."

An Mei shook her head. "I can't," she said, wiping her face with the sleeve of her ragged jacket. "I can't ever come to school again," and she began to cry harder.

"Step in here and wait," said the maid. "I have to go to the kitchen for another tray. The cook will be cross with me if I don't come. As soon as possible, I will tell Mrs. Li you are here."

An Mei stepped into the hall. She forgot to cry now as she looked in wonder about her. What a huge vase! And such beautiful flowers—real ones! No wonder she could not sell the ones her mother made!

An Mei could smell food, and it made her stomach feel worse than ever. She could hear

---

Li (lē)

women's voices and the tinkling of dishes. One woman's voice stood out over the others.

"She told me just this morning. I was so shocked! 'I can't work for you anymore, because I have a chance to go to America.' "

There followed a murmur of sympathetic voices. "Good cooks are hard to find," said another voice that sounded like Mrs. Li's.

And then before An Mei had stopped wondering about the strangeness and beauty around her, she saw Mrs. Li coming toward her. She looked beautiful in an orange and black Chinese dress.

"Oh, my dear," she said kindly, "school is not until one o'clock. You are very welcome to come at that time, but—"

An Mei shook her head, fighting back the tears. "I cannot come, not ever again. Mother says I must sell flowers so we can eat. Yesterday I did not sell any at all."

"So you did not eat?" questioned the lady softly.

An Mei nodded.

"Then you shall eat here with me," said Mrs. Li, holding out her hand to An Mei. Trembling with wonder and shyness, An Mei walked beside the

sympathetic—*a feeling in agreement with someone or something*

Chinese woman into a big room where many ladies in beautiful clothes were drinking tea. They all stopped talking and looked at An Mei.

"This is one of the school children. She is selling flowers her mother has made. Maybe you would like to look at them while I give her some tea and cakes." One of the ladies took An Mei's flowers.

An Mei felt as if she were dreaming. It could not be real—the delicious cakes, the fragrant tea, the kindness of the ladies.

The chattering had begun again. Mrs. Li left her after a few minutes with the plate of cakes. An Mei tried not to eat too many, but they were so good, and she was so hungry. She was just beginning to eat her fourth one when Mrs. Li came back. Another woman was with her.

Mrs. Li put a pile of coins on the table. "The ladies bought all your flowers," she explained. "Now you can come to school with the other children this afternoon."

An Mei could not believe her eyes and ears. She could not even find her tongue to say thank you.

"About your mother," said the other woman, sitting down beside An Mei, "Can she cook?"

"Oh, yes!" answered An Mei. "When we lived in China, she cooked at a restaurant."

"Is yours a large family?" she continued.

An Mei shook her head. "No, just Mother and I are left."

The woman looked at Mrs. Li. "I think God is answering my prayer more quickly than I thought possible." She turned to An Mei. "Will you bring your mother to see me this evening? I live just three houses from here on the corner. Tell her that I need a cook right away. I provide a room and food plus a small wage. You could help in the mornings and go to school in the after-noons."

"Thank You, Jesus, thank You, thank You!" breathed An Mei over and over again as she ran down the streets to tell her mother the wonderful news. She knew she would never stop thanking Him as long as she lived!

---

wage—*money for work done*

Thinking It Through

1. What did An Mei do each day to help her mother earn money?

2. Why couldn't An Mei go to school?

3. What kind of home did An Mei and her mother have?

4. Why did An Mei go back to the big yellow house the second day?

5. What kind of school was being held in the garden at the yellow house?

6. What did An Mei's mother say about the school?

7. What words did An Mei say even though she didn't understand them?

8. How did God provide for An Mei and her mother?

The Matchless Pearl

Author Unknown

A heavy splash was followed
by many ripples, and then the water below
the pier was still. An American businessman
crouched on the low pier on a bay in India. His
eyes were riveted to the water, straining to see his
Indian friend swimming in the deep.

riveted—*firmly fixed*

146

In a moment, a dark head appeared. Then the old Indian pearl diver clambered onto the dock, grinning as he shook off the water.

"This will be a good one," said Rambhau, handing a large oyster to Morris.

Prying open the shell, Morris exclaimed, "Have you ever seen a better pearl! It's perfect, isn't it?"

"There are better pearls, much better. Why, I have one that—" Rambhau's voice trailed off. "See this—the black speck here, and that tiny dent. It's just as you say about your God. People look perfect to themselves, but God sees all the imperfections."

As the two men started down the road, another man walked far ahead of them.

"Do you see that man over there?" asked Rambhau. "He's a pilgrim going perhaps to Bombay or Calcutta. He walks barefooted and picks the sharpest stones—and see," he pointed, "every few blocks he kneels down and kisses the road. That is good. The first day of the New Year I also will begin my pilgrimage to Delhi. I will suffer, but it will be sweet, for it will purchase Heaven for me."

Rambhau (räm·bou′)
Bombay—*a city of India*
Calcutta—*a city of India*

pilgrimage—*a journey made to a place thought to be holy*
Delhi (dĕl′ē)—*a city of India*

"Rambhau!" said Morris. "You can't purchase Heaven! Jesus Christ died to provide Heaven for you!" But the conversation seemed useless. The old man could not understand.

One afternoon not long afterwards, Morris answered a knock on his door and found Rambhau standing there.

"Will you come to my house for a short time?" asked the diver. "I have something to show you."

Morris followed him to his home. Once they were there, Rambhau brought out a small but heavy strongbox. "I have had this box for years," he said. "I keep only one thing in it."

The old man drew a carefully wrapped package out of the box. Gently he folded back layers of cloth. Uncovering a brilliant pearl, he placed it carefully in Morris's hands.

The pearl glowed with a luster Morris had never seen before. It would have brought a fabulous sum in any market.

"Now I will tell you about it," Rambhau said. "Once I had a son."

luster—*brightness*

148

"A son?" Morris interrupted. "You've never said a word about him!"

"No. I couldn't. But now I must tell you. My son was the best pearl diver on the coasts of India. What joy he brought me! He always dreamed of finding a pearl beyond all that had ever been found. One day he found it. But finding that pearl cost him his life.

"All these years I've kept this pearl," Rambhau continued. "And now I want to give this pearl to you, because you are my best friend."

Morris looked up excitedly. "Rambhau, you can't *give* me the pearl! How can I accept this priceless gift? Let me buy it from you. I will give you all I can."

"What are you saying?" The older diver was stunned. "You don't understand, my friend. Don't you see? My only son gave his life to get this pearl. I cannot sell it. But I want to give it to you because of my love for you."

Morris could not speak. He gripped his old friend's hand. "Rambhau, don't you see? That is just what you have been saying to God all these years."

Rambhau stared at Morris for a long time. But slowly he began to understand.

"You have tried to buy salvation from God. But God is offering salvation to you as a free

149

gift," Morris explained. "It is so great and price-less that no man on earth could buy it, and no man is good enough to deserve it. It cost God the life blood of His only Son, so that you could enter into Heaven. All you can do is to accept God's gift because of His great love for you."

Tears were rolling down the old man's cheeks. "Now I understand," he said. "Some things are too priceless to be bought. I will accept God's salvation."

Rambhau bowed his head in prayer to receive Jesus Christ as his Savior. After he had prayed, Morris took a small Bible from his pocket and read aloud:

> "For when we were yet without strength, in due time Christ died for the ungodly. For scarcely for a righteous man will one die: yet peradventure for a good man some would even dare to die. But God commendeth His love toward us, in that, while we were yet sinners, Christ died for us."
> *(Romans 5:6–8)*

> "And this is the record, that God hath given to us eternal life, and this life is in His Son. He that hath the Son hath life; and he that hath not the Son of God hath not life."
> *(1 John 5:11–12)*

---

peradventure—*perhaps, possibly*
commendeth—*shows*

"For by grace are ye saved through faith; and that not of yourselves: it is the gift of God: Not of works, lest any man should boast." *(Ephesians 2:8–9)*

Character Theme—Friendship, Generosity, & Faith

Thinking It Through

1. What was Rambhau looking for underwater?

2. Where are pearls found?

3. What had Morris been trying to help Rambhau to understand?

4. How did Rambhau plan to get into Heaven?

5. What priceless gift did Rambhau give to Morris?

6. Why did the pearl have so much meaning to Rambhau?

7. How did Morris use the pearl to help Rambhau understand salvation?

RAZAKA:
Son of the Chief
Grace Helen Davis

Razaka, son of the village chief, sneaked around a corner of the mud hut. He ran quietly on his bare, brown tiptoes, for he wanted to scare the group of younger children he saw playing before they saw him coming. He picked up a stick and threw it, hoping it would hit someone. But one of the children happened to look up just as the stick left Razaka's hand. In a flash, they were all running in different directions.

"Well, I'll catch them another time," Razaka said to himself. "It's fun to make smaller children run and cry. And no one dares hurt me, because I'm the son of the powerful chief of our village!"

Razaka lived in a village on the island of Madagascar 150 years ago. In those days the people of the larger African island made slaves of their neighbors if they could.

But Razaka was wilder and more cruel than other boys of his age. He was strong and so full

---

Razaka (rä·zä′kə)　　　　**Madagascar** (măd′ə·găs′kər)

152

of pep he didn't know what to do with himself. His father was proud of Razaka's strength and handsome looks, and he did not punish Razaka when he was told by people how mean the boy acted.

"Oh, my son will settle down after a while," the chief said. "He's just a boy who wants to have a good time."

Now Razaka made his way down the village path, still looking for mischief. He saw a blind girl in her doorway, and he went and pulled her black hair, so that she cried. Then he threw a

stone at a lemur and laughed as the creature ran chattering up a tree.

"All the people and the animals are afraid of me," Razaka thought, grinning.

Soon he reached his own home. Razaka kicked a goat tied in the yard and went inside.

"Hail, my Father," said Razaka, as he had been taught. His father was one person he did not dare to disobey.

"Ah, Son, I have something to say to you. How would you like to give up your easy, roaming ways and settle down and learn from the English people?"

Razaka jumped. Give up his freedom to run and play? "I don't know, Father," he answered slowly.

But as his father talked, Razaka listened carefully. The chief had met some missionaries from England. They were telling the people of Madagascar about a different God, but Razaka's father was not interested in that. However, the chief was interested in the school the missionaries were starting. In the school they would teach the boys and girls to read and write in their own language, Malagasy.

---

lemur—*a furry animal with large eyes and a long tail. Many lemurs look like monkeys.*

Malagasy (măl′ə·găs′ē)

As his father talked, Razaka frowned in puzzlement. He had never heard of reading and writing. Well, at least it would give him a chance to find out things the other boys in the tribe didn't know. "I think I would like to try the English people's school, Father, if it is your wish," Razaka decided.

"It is my wish, Son," replied his father.

That is how it happened that Razaka was one of the first pupils at the school which the English missionaries started. Razaka found it very hard to sit still and put little marks on paper or read them from a book. Sometimes he felt like getting up and running off to hunt game or to tease someone. But he didn't do it, because he wanted to learn what those marks meant.

But outside of class, Razaka was still mean. He began to beat up the other students. The teachers tried to stop him, but Razaka wouldn't listen to them.

Then one day he learned to write his name, and the long name of his village. He learned to read short sentences, too, and to do sums in arithmetic, and to know something of the world in which he lived.

The teachers at the mission school also told about God and His Son, Jesus Christ, but Razaka kept his ears closed to that. His people worshiped all kinds of spirits, and Razaka figured that their religion was good enough for him.

Time passed, and Razaka learned so well that he was able to read in the Bible. His teacher gave him a part of the New Testament in Malagasy, and Razaka read it whenever he got a chance. He liked to read, and he began to spend more time now reading and less time being mean to others.

"This isn't an easy book to read, but I can make it out," he boasted when he visited his father and mother.

"That's fine, Son," they replied. Razaka's father was very proud of a son who could make words out of the strange marks in a book.

But as he got into the New Testament, Razaka began to notice something besides words and sentences. This was the story of a Man's life and teachings, and they were both just the opposite of Razaka's.

"What a softy Jesus was, always saying to be kind to others and going about helping people Himself!" Razaka thought as he read.

Yet he found there was something about Jesus that he liked. He began to wonder if Jesus' way of being kind to people wasn't better than his way of scaring people.

"That must be a difficult book, Razaka," his mother said one day when she saw him thinking in that way.

Razaka's brown face flushed. "Yes, Mother; the things in it are hard to understand," he told her.

He didn't want to let his folks know that he was beginning to like this Jesus whom he had called a softy at first. He began to try to read just the words of the Book and not think about its stories, but he couldn't forget Jesus.

His own life began to change. "Razaka no longer acts so mean," the children said in surprise. The missionary teachers noticed it, too, and tried to help Razaka give his heart to Jesus. At first he wouldn't, but as he read on into the Gospels, he knew he was reading about the true God.

"I believe on Jesus Christ as my Savior," Razaka, the chief's son said one day. "He is the true and the living God. I'm going to live for Him."

When Razaka went home and told his father, the chief became very angry.

"This is no time for you to become a Christian, my son," the chief said. "Don't you know that our new ruler, Queen Ranavalona, wants us to keep to the old religion?"

Ranavalona (rä·nä·və·lō′nə)

"Yes, Father, but I belong to Jesus Christ now. He is greater than our ruler, and I must obey Him," Razaka answered.

However, what the chief had said about the new queen was true. Queen Ranavalona wanted the people to turn away from Christianity and back to their spirit worship. Before long she passed a new law that all Bibles and New Testaments must be burned.

Rather than burn God's Word, Razaka left home. He lost his New Testament, but one day one of the Christians put a whole Bible into his hands. "Guard this, Razaka," he said. "It is one of the few Bibles in our language."

When the Christian who gave him a Bible was put to death, Razaka became leader of the Christians. He lived in a large cave, and there he studied the Bible diligently.

Then news came that the wicked queen was dead and that the new ruler was changing what she had done and asked the missionaries to return.

"Thank God!" said Razaka. He left the cave and became a great Christian worker in Madagascar. He is still remembered for the churches he built and the work he did. He always loved and taught the Bible, which he knew so well that he was nicknamed "the Bible with legs."

Character Theme—Faith & Courage

Thinking It Through

1. Where did Razaka live?
2. Why did Razaka think he could get away with being cruel to others?
3. Why did Razaka agree to go to the English missionaries' school?
4. What was Razaka's first opinion about Jesus?
5. What did Razaka finally do after reading more of the Bible?
6. Rather than allow God's Word to be burned, what did Razaka do?
7. What nickname was given to Razaka?

Missionaries

Author Unknown

Away in foreign lands they wondered how
    Their single word had power!
At home, the Christians, two or three, had met
    To pray an hour.

---

foreign—*of another country*

When Livingstone Was Lost

Hugh T. Kerr

David Livingstone was a famous missionary doctor in the darkest part of Africa for over thirty years. Near the end of his life, the world lost track of him. For two and a half years, not a single word came from him or about him, and his many admirers in England, the United States, and other lands thought he was dead.

He was lost. For years he had received no word from his home nor from the great world that was hidden from him in the African jungles.

He had been trying to rid Africa of the slave trade, and his heart was sick and sad. He was hungry and lonely. His feet were worn, and every step pained him. Some of his servants betrayed him and tried to kill him. They threw spears at him, and three times one day he narrowly escaped

161

death. He felt as if he were dying on his feet. His goods had been stolen and sold, and he himself was just a skeleton.

Then something happened!

Over in Paris there was a man by the name of James Gordon Bennett. He was the editor of a great American newspaper called the *New York Herald*. He knew that thousands of people were interested in Livingstone's story, and he thought if he could find something out about where he was, people would like to read it in his newspaper. He sent a telegram to Russia and asked a man to come and talk the matter over with him. The man was an Englishman named Henry M. Stanley.

When Mr. Stanley arrived, Mr. Bennett said, "Where do you think Livingstone is?"

Mr. Stanley said he did not know, and that was the truth, for no white man but Livingstone himself knew.

Then Mr. Bennett said, "I want you to find Livingstone. Here is some money. When you need more, you may have it, just as much as you need. Never mind about how much it costs, only find Livingstone."

Stanley took with him 200 men with all kinds of food and other supplies and started out. He

---

Paris—*the capital city of France*

nearly perished in his journey into Africa. At last one day, just when Livingstone was ready to give up, one of his servants came running into the missionary doctor's tent all excited and gasped, "An Englishman; I see him."

And sure enough, he did. In a little while, Stanley came, and Livingstone could scarcely believe his eyes or his ears as the handsome white man came forward with open hands saying, "Dr. Livingstone, I presume?"

---

perished—*died*

163

Those were great days for the poor, sick missionary. He grew rapidly well. He had good things to eat and enjoyed the fine new clothes Stanley gave him. Soon he was like a new man, talking and telling stories and hearing about the wonderful things that had happened since he last heard from home.

"You have brought me new life," Dr. Livingstone kept saying to Mr. Stanley.

Together they visited the sights of Africa and held what Dr. Livingstone called picnics, and for six months Stanley came to know by observing Dr. Livingstone what a real Christian was. Stanley himself became a Christian through Dr. Livingstone's testimony, and for a while he served as a missionary himself. When he was ready to return, he wanted Dr. Livingstone to go home with him, but the great doctor said his work was not done and he could not leave.

The time came to say good-bye. They had been walking side by side. Stanley took Livingstone's hand in his and said, "Now, my dear Doctor, the best of friends must part: you have come far enough; let me beg of you to turn back."

Livingstone replied, "I am grateful to you for what you have done for me. God guide you safely home and bless you, my friend."

"And may God bring you safely back to us all, my dear friend. Farewell," said Stanley.

Livingstone turned back to his work and to his loneliness, and Stanley went on to tell the great wide world of the wonderful man he had left behind, all alone, in Africa. They never saw each other again. Livingstone never returned home but went on with his work among his black friends. What a brave, true, wonderful man he was!

Two days after Stanley had gone, Dr. Livingstone was alone again. It was his birthday. Did I say he was alone? If you will read his journal in which he wrote something nearly every day, you will find that on that day he wrote this:

"March 19th. My birthday; my Jesus: my King: my Life: my All. I again dedicate my whole self to Thee. Accept me. And grant, O gracious Father, that ere the year is gone I may finish my work. In Jesus' name I ask it. Amen."

After all, you see, he was not alone. Jesus was with him.

David Livingstone lived and worked for a little more than a year after he said good-bye to Stanley, and then one morning his faithful black

---

ere—*before*

servants found him kneeling beside his bed in his tent. The great doctor was so still and quiet that the servants touched him, but he did not move.

He had died on his knees in prayer. That was a fitting end to his wonderful life, because Dr. Livingstone was always praying. He was a man of God.

Character Theme—Faithfulness & Service

Thinking It Through

1. To what continent did David Livingstone go as a missionary?

2. After Dr. Livingstone had been in Africa for several years, why did the world think that he was dead?

3. Why was Henry Stanley sent to Africa?

4. In what condition did Mr. Stanley find David Livingstone?

5. How long did Stanley stay in Africa with Dr. Livingstone?

6. Why was it fitting that Dr. Livingstone had been praying when he died?

From the Bible

. . . In every thing by prayer and supplication with thanksgiving let your requests be made known unto God.

—*Philippians 4:6*

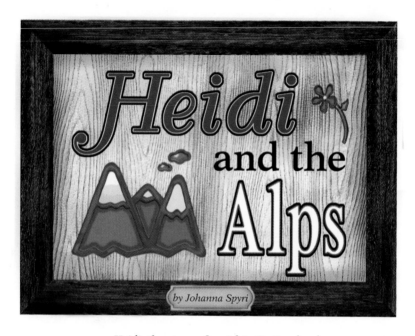

Heidi and the Alps

by Johanna Spyri

Heidi, the story of a girl in Switzerland who goes to live with her grandfather high in the Alps mountains, has been a favorite book for many years. You will enjoy checking it out of the library and reading it.

High on the Alps there once lived an old man all alone. His hut stood on a jutting cliff exposed to wind and sun alike and overlooking the beautiful valley below.

The old man had placed a bench on the side of his hut toward the valley. Here he sat resting one day when suddenly he saw a little girl running toward him.

"Good morning, Grandfather," she said. "I am Heidi, and I have come to stay with you. My aunt has shown me the way up the mountain."

"Well, well, what does this mean?" said the old man. The child stood before him patiently waiting, with her hands folded behind her back.

"What would you like to do?" asked the grandfather kindly, after he had recovered from his surprise.

"I should like to go into the hut and see what you have there," answered the little girl.

"Take up your bundle then and come!"

Heidi followed her grandfather into the one room of the little house.

"Where shall I sleep, Grandfather?" she asked.

"Where you like," was his answer.

She ran about looking into every nook and corner. Near her grandfather's bed was a ladder which led to the loft. Up climbed Heidi and found herself in a little room half filled with fragrant hay. Through a small, round window she could see for miles across the valley below.

"I shall sleep here," she cried. "Oh, it is beautiful. Come up, Grandfather, and see how beautiful it is." Then she ran busily about and piled the hay in a neat little bed by the window.

"Now, I have my bed made," she called down, "and I need sheets and a cover."

_____

fragrant—*sweet-smelling*

"Well, well," said the old man, who was really pleased with the quick and helpful child. With his arms full of bedclothes he climbed the ladder and helped Heidi make a comfortable bed.

The little girl looked on with admiration. "How I wish it were night so that I could lie down!" she exclaimed.

"We had better have something to eat first," said her grandfather.

All at once Heidi felt very hungry. "I think so, too."

Soon a bright fire was burning in the open fireplace, and the kettle boiled merrily. The old man put a piece of cheese on a long fork, and held it over the coals until it was a golden yellow on all sides.

Heidi ran to the cupboard where she had seen the bread and the dishes. When her grandfather came with the toasted cheese and the cup of tea, the table was nicely laid with the loaf of bread in the middle.

"You can think what to do without being told," said the old man, "and that is good." Then he filled a bowl with goat's milk for Heidi, and spread her bread thickly with hot cheese.

When they had finished their dinner, the old man put everything in order in the hut and in the goats' house. Heidi followed him, observing very closely all that he did.

As evening came on, the wind began to sigh through the great pine trees. It sounded so beautiful to Heidi that she ran out of the hut and began to skip and dance about. She felt very happy.

"Now, Heidi," Grandfather said, "you must go to bed. Go and sleep soundly."

Heidi said good night to her grandfather and to the goats. She climbed the ladder and was soon fast asleep on her bed of fragrant hay.

The old man went to Heidi's bedside. There she lay fast asleep. She must have been dreaming pleasant dreams, for a look of happiness was on her little face. The grandfather stood for a long time, looking down at the sleeping child. Then he turned and went down the ladder.

When Heidi opened her eyes the next morning, the sun was shining in through the little round window of her room. She dressed quickly and went out in front of the hut. There was Peter, with his flock of goats, ready to go up the mountain.

"Would you like to go to the pasture with Peter and the goats?" asked her grandfather.

The child danced with delight. "Then eat your breakfast and be ready. You must be clean, or the sun will laugh at you," said the old man, as he went into the hut to prepare the lunch.

The two children went merrily up the mountain. The sky was deep blue, and in the center stood the bright sun, sparkling upon the green Alps.

Heidi ran hither and thither and shouted with joy. The mountain path glistened with beautiful gentians. In her delight over all the glittering, nodding blossoms, Heidi even forgot the goats and Peter, too.

So Peter had to look on all sides, and his round eyes, that did not move quickly from one thing to another, had more work than they could well manage. The goats also ran here and there, and the boy whistled and called and swung his staff to drive all the runaways together.

"Come here, Heidi," shouted Peter. "We have still a long way to climb."

Higher and higher they climbed until they came to the green grass where the goats usually pastured for the day.

Heidi sat down on the grass and looked

---

hither and thither—*here and there*
glistened—*shone; sparkled*

gentian (gĕn′shən)—
a flowering plant

about her. In front of her a great, wide field of snow rose up toward the deep blue heavens, and a high tower of rocks seemed to look sternly down upon her.

For a long time she sat gazing at the rocks—so long that the lofty crags seemed to have faces and to be looking down at her like old friends.

Suddenly, at Peter's whistle, the goats came jumping down the mountain. Heidi sprang up and ran towards them. She saw that her grandfather's goats, Little Swan and Little Bear, as they were called, were the finest in the flock.

"Of course they are," Peter said, "for your grandfather feeds them salt and washes them and has the best shed to keep them in." Peter knew each goat by name and could tell all its curious ways.

The white goat was milked for the noonday meal, and the children set out their bread and cheese upon the grass. Away bounded the goats again, climbing the rocky heights.

And so the day passed until the sun was beginning to sink down behind the mountains. Suddenly all the grass became golden, and the rocks above began to flash with rosy lights.

"Oh, look, Peter," shouted the child. "All the mountains are burning! Look at the rocks! See the beautiful snow! Everything is on fire."

"It is always so," answered Peter, good-naturedly; "but it is not fire. It will be just the same tomorrow."

Peter whistled and called the goats together, and they started down the mountain. Heidi was silent until she reached the hut and saw her grandfather sitting under the fir tree.

"Oh, Grandfather, the mountains are beautiful," she called out, even before she had reached him. "I saw the fire and the roses on the cliffs, and the blue and yellow flowers." Then she asked about the fire which she had seen at sunset.

---

good-naturedly—*pleasantly*

"It is the sunshine," her grandfather explained. "When the sun says good night to the mountains, he throws his most beautiful beams across them so that they may not forget that he is coming back in the morning."

This pleased the little girl and she could hardly wait for the morrow to come so that she could go to the pasture again and see the sun bid good night to the mountains.

Character Theme—Cheerfulness &
Contentment

Thinking It Through

1. Did Grandfather know that Heidi was coming to live with him?

2. Where did Heidi decide she would like to sleep?

3. How did Heidi show her grandfather that she could "think what to do without being told"?

4. What did Heidi do her first full day in the mountains?

5. Why did Heidi think the mountains were burning?

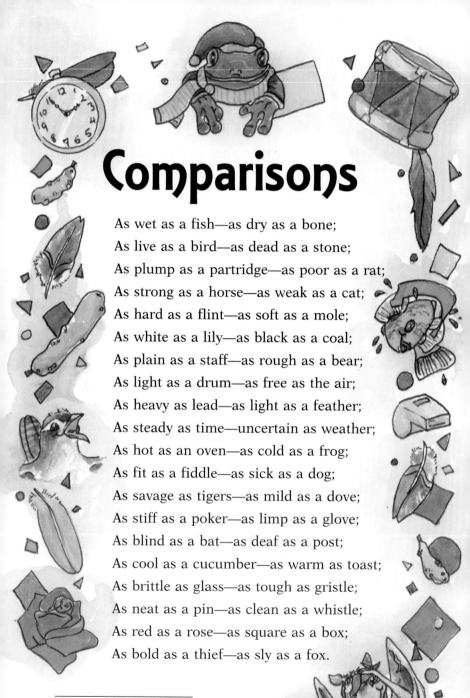

Comparisons

As wet as a fish—as dry as a bone;
As live as a bird—as dead as a stone;
As plump as a partridge—as poor as a rat;
As strong as a horse—as weak as a cat;
As hard as a flint—as soft as a mole;
As white as a lily—as black as a coal;
As plain as a staff—as rough as a bear;
As light as a drum—as free as the air;
As heavy as lead—as light as a feather;
As steady as time—uncertain as weather;
As hot as an oven—as cold as a frog;
As fit as a fiddle—as sick as a dog;
As savage as tigers—as mild as a dove;
As stiff as a poker—as limp as a glove;
As blind as a bat—as deaf as a post;
As cool as a cucumber—as warm as toast;
As brittle as glass—as tough as gristle;
As neat as a pin—as clean as a whistle;
As red as a rose—as square as a box;
As bold as a thief—as sly as a fox.

savage—*wild; untamed*
poker—*a metal bar used to stir a fire*
gristle—*tough, white tissue found in meat*

176

JO MAKES A CALL

Louisa May Alcott

Jo is really Louisa May Alcott herself as a girl, and Meg, Beth, and Amy are her sisters. In this story from *Little Women*, Jo decides to cheer up the sick Laurence boy, who lives in the big house next door.

"What in the world are you going to do now, Jo?" asked Meg, one snowy afternoon, as her sister came tramping through the hall in rubber boots, old coat and hood, with a broom in one hand and a shovel in the other.

"Going out for exercise," answered Jo, with a mischievous twinkle in her eyes.

"I should think two long walks this morning would have been enough! It's cold and dull out; and I advise you to stay warm and dry by the fire, as I do," said Meg with a shiver.

"Never take advice! Can't keep still all day and, not being a cat, I don't like to doze by the

---

mischievous—*teasing*

177

fire. I like adventures, and I'm going to find some."

Meg went back to toast her feet and read *Ivanhoe,* and Jo began to dig paths with great energy. The snow was light, and with her broom she soon swept a path all round the garden for Beth to walk in when the sun came out and the invalid dolls needed air. Now, the garden separated the Marches' house from that of Mr. Laurence. Both stood in a suburb of the city, which was still country-like, with groves and lawns, large gardens, and quiet streets.

A low hedge parted the two estates. On one side was an old brown house, looking rather bare and shabby, robbed of the vines that in summer covered its walls, and the flowers which then surrounded it. On the other side was a stately stone mansion, plainly having every sort of comfort and luxury, from the big coach house and well-kept grounds to the conservatory and the glimpses of lovely things one caught between the rich curtains. Yet it seemed a lonely, lifeless sort of house; for no children played on the lawn, no motherly face ever smiled at the windows, and

---

Ivanhoe (ī'vən·hō)
suburb—*an area on the outskirts of a city; often a small town itself*

conservatory—*a room enclosed in glass for growing plants*

few people went in and out, except the old gentleman and his grandson.

To Jo's lively fancy, this fine house seemed a
kind of enchanted palace, full of splendors and
delights, which no one enjoyed. She had long
wanted to behold these hidden glories and to
know the "Laurence boy," who looked as if he
would like to be known, if he only knew how to
begin. He had not been seen lately, and Jo began
to think he had gone away, when she one day
spied a brown face at the upper window, looking
wistfully down into their garden where Beth and
Amy were snowballing one another.

"That boy is suffering for society and fun,"
she said to herself. "His grandpa does not know
what's good for him and keeps him shut up all
alone. He needs a party of jolly boys to play
with, or somebody young and lively. I've a great
mind to go over and tell the old gentleman so!"

The idea amused Jo, who liked to do daring
things. The plan of "going over" was not forgotten, and when the snowy afternoon came, Jo
resolved to see what could be done. She saw
Mr. Laurence drive off, and then sallied out to
dig her way down to the hedge, where she paused

---

splendor—*richness;
beautiful appearance*

sallied—*rushed out*

and took a survey. All quiet—curtains down at the lower windows; servants out of sight and nothing human visible but a curly black head leaning on a thin hand at the upper window.

"There he is," thought Jo, "poor boy! all alone and sick this dismal day. It's a shame! I'll toss up a snowball and make him look out, and then say a kind word to him."

Up went a handful of soft snow, and the head turned at once, showing a face which lost its listless look in a minute, as the big eyes brightened and the mouth began to smile. Jo nodded and laughed and flourished her broom as she called out:

"How do you do? Are you sick?"

Laurie opened the window and croaked out as hoarsely as a raven:

"Better, thank you. I've had a bad cold and been shut up a week."

"I'm sorry. What do you amuse yourself with?"

"Nothing; it's as dull as tombs up here."

"Don't you read?"

"Not much; they won't let me."

"Can't somebody read to you?"

"Grandpa does, sometimes; but my books

---

survey—*a detailed study*
dismal—*dark and gloomy; dreary*

listless—*having no interest in what is going on around one* don't interest him, and I hate to ask Brooke all the time."

"Have someone come and see you, then."

"There isn't anyone I'd like to see. Boys make such a row, and my head is weak."

"Isn't there some nice girl who'd read and amuse you? Girls are quiet, and like to play nurse."

"Don't know any."

"You know us," began Jo, then laughed and stopped.

"So I do! Will you come, please?" cried Laurie.

"I'm not quiet and nice; but I'll come, if Mother will let me. I'll go ask her. Shut that window, like a good boy, and wait till I come."

With that, Jo shouldered her broom and marched into the house, wondering what they would all say to her. Laurie was in a flutter of excitement at the idea of having company and flew about to get ready; as Mrs. March said, he was "a little gentleman," and did honor to the coming guest by brushing his curly hair, putting on a fresh collar, and trying to tidy up the room, which, in spite of half a dozen servants, was anything but neat. Presently there came a loud ring, then a decided voice asking for "Mr. Laurie," and a surprised-looking servant came running up to announce a young lady.

"All right, show her up. It's Miss Jo," said
Laurie, going to the door of his little parlor to
meet Jo, who appeared, looking rosy and kind and
quite at her ease, with a covered dish in one hand
and Beth's three kittens in the other.

"Here I am, bag and baggage," she said briskly.
"Mother sent her love, and was glad if I could do
anything for you. Meg wanted me to bring some
of her special dessert; and Beth thought her cats
would be comforting. I knew you'd laugh at
them, but I couldn't refuse, she was so anxious to
do something."

It so happened that Beth's funny loan was
just the thing; for, in laughing over the kittens
Laurie forgot his bashfulness and
grew sociable at once.

"That looks too pretty to eat," he said, smiling with pleasure, as Jo uncovered the dish and showed the gelatin dessert, surrounded by a garland of green leaves and the scarlet flowers of Amy's pet geranium.

"It isn't anything, only they all felt kindly and wanted to show it. Tell the girl to put it away for your tea. It's so simple, you can eat it; and, being soft, it will slip down without hurting your sore throat. What a cozy room this is!"

"It might be if it was kept nice; but the maids are lazy and I don't know how to make them mind. It worries me, though."

"I'll right it up in two minutes; for it only needs to have the hearth brushed, so, —and the things made straight on the mantelpiece, so, —and the books put here, and the bottles there, and your sofa turned from the light, and the pillows plumped up a bit. Now then, you're fixed."

And so he was; for, as she laughed and talked, Jo had whisked things into place and given quite a different air to the room. Laurie watched her in respectful silence and when she beckoned him to his sofa, he sat down with a sigh of satisfaction, saying gratefully:

---

sociable—*friendly; agreeable*

"How kind you are! Yes, that's what it wanted. Now please take the big chair and let me do something to amuse my company."

"No; I came to amuse you. Shall I read aloud?" and Jo looked affectionately toward some inviting books nearby.

"Thank you; I've read all those and, if you don't mind, I'd rather talk," answered Laurie.

"Not a bit; I'll talk all day if you'll only set me going. Beth says I never know when to stop."

"Is Beth the rosy one, who stays at home a good deal, and sometimes goes out with a little basket?" asked Laurie, with interest.

"Yes, that's Beth; she's my girl, and a regular good one she is, too."

"The pretty one is Meg and the curly-haired one is Amy, I believe?"

"How did you find out?"

Laurie colored up, but answered frankly, "Why, you see, I often hear you calling to one another, and when I'm alone up here I can't help looking over at your house, you always seem to be having such good times. I beg your pardon for being so rude, but sometimes you forget to put down the curtain at the window where the flowers are; and when the lamps are lighted, it's like looking at a picture to see the fire, and you all round the table with your mother; her face is right opposite, and it looks so sweet behind the flowers I can't help watching it. I haven't got any mother, you know;" and Laurie poked the fire to hide a twitching of the lips that he could not control.

Read the entire heart-warming book, *Little Women,* to share in the adventures of Jo and her sisters.

Character Theme—Encouragement, Friendship, & Kindness

Thinking It Through

1. Why did Meg think that Jo ought to stay indoors?

2. Who lived next door to Jo and her family?

3. Why did Jo think that the grandson was "suffering for society and fun"?

4. How did Jo get Laurie's attention that day?

5. What did Jo take with her for the visit with Laurie?

6. How did Laurie know the girls' names and who they were?

A Kitten

Eleanor Farjeon

He's nothing much but fur
And two round eyes of blue,
He has a giant purr
And a midget mew.

He darts and pats the air,
He starts and cocks his ear,
When there is nothing there
For him to see and hear.

He runs around in rings,
But why we cannot tell;
With sideways leaps he springs
At things invisible—

Then half-way through a leap
His startled eyeballs close,
And he drops off to sleep
With one paw on his nose.

Down the Rabbit Hole

from *Alice in Wonderland*
Lewis Carroll

In this first chapter of *Alice in Wonderland,* we learn how Alice's strange and wonderful dream began.

Alice was beginning to get very tired of sitting by her sister on the bank, and of having nothing to do. Once or twice she had peeped into the book her sister was reading, but it had no pictures or conversations in it, "and what is the use of a book," thought Alice, "without pictures or conversations?"

So she was considering in her own mind (as well as she could, for the hot day made her feel very sleepy) whether the pleasure of making a daisy chain would be worth the trouble of getting up and picking the daisies, when suddenly a white rabbit with pink eyes ran close by her.

"Oh, dear! Oh, dear! I shall be too late!" cried the Rabbit, taking a watch out of his pocket and looking at it. Alice started to her feet, for it flashed across her mind that she had never before seen a rabbit with either a waistcoat pocket or a watch to

waistcoat—*a vestlike, sleeveless jacket*

take out of it, and, burning with curiosity, she ran across the field after it, and was just in time to see it pop down a large rabbit hole under the hedge.

In another moment down went Alice after it, never once considering how in the world she was to get out again.

The rabbit hole went straight on like a tunnel for some way, and then dipped suddenly down, so suddenly that Alice had not a moment to think about stopping herself before she found herself falling down what seemed to be a very deep well.

Either the well was very deep, or she fell very slowly, for she had plenty of time as she went down to look about her, and to wonder what was going to happen next. First she tried to look down and make out what she was coming to, but it was too dark to see anything; then she looked at

the sides of the well, and noticed that they were filled with cupboards and bookshelves; here and there she saw maps and pictures hung upon pegs.

Down, down, down. Would the fall *never* come to an end? "I wonder how many miles I've fallen by this time?" she said aloud. "I must be getting somewhere near the center of the earth. I wonder if I shall fall right *through* the earth! How funny it'll seem to come out among the people that walk with their heads downward! I shall have to ask them what the name of the country is, you know. 'Please, ma'am, is this New Zealand or Australia?' And what an ignorant little girl she'll think me for asking! No, it'll never do to ask; perhaps I shall see it written up somewhere."

Down, down, down. There was nothing else to do, so Alice soon began talking again. "Dinah'll miss me very much tonight, I should think!" (Dinah was the cat.) "I hope they'll remember her saucer of milk at teatime. Dinah, my dear! I wish you were down here with me! There are no mice in the air, I'm afraid, but you might catch a bat, and that's very like a mouse, you know. But do cats eat bats, I wonder?" And here Alice began to get rather sleepy, and went on saying to herself, in a dreamy sort of way, "Do cats eat bats? Do cats eat bats?" and sometimes, "Do bats eat cats?" for, you see, as she couldn't answer either question, it didn't much matter which way she put it. She felt that she was dozing off, and had just begun to dream that she was walking hand in hand with Dinah, and was saying to her very earnestly, "Now, Dinah, tell me the truth, did you ever eat a bat?" when suddenly, thump! thump! down she came upon a heap of sticks and dry leaves, and the fall was over.

Alice was not a bit hurt, and she jumped up onto her feet in a moment; she looked up, but it was dark overhead; before her was another long passage, and the White Rabbit was still in sight, hurrying down it. There was not a moment to be lost: away went Alice like the wind, and was just in time to hear it say, as it turned a corner, "Oh, my ears and whiskers, how late it's getting!" She was close behind it when she turned the corner, but the

Rabbit was no longer to be seen: she found herself in a long, low hall, which was lit up by a row of lamps hanging from the roof.

There were doors all round the hall, but they were all locked, and when Alice had been all the way down one side and up the other, trying every door, she walked sadly down the middle, wondering how she was ever to get out again.

Suddenly she came upon a little three-legged table, all made of solid glass; there was nothing on it but a tiny golden key, and Alice's first idea was that this might belong to one of the doors of the hall; but, alas! either the locks were too large, or the key was too small, but at any rate it would not open any of them. However, on the second time round she came upon a low curtain she had not noticed before, and behind it was a little door about fifteen inches high; she tried the little golden key in the lock, and to her great delight it fit!

Alice opened the door and found that it led into a small passage, not much larger than a rat hole; she knelt down and looked along the passage into the loveliest garden you ever saw. How she longed to get out of that dark hall, and wander about among those beds of bright flowers and those cool fountains. But she could not even get her head through the doorway. "And even if my head would go through," thought poor Alice, "it would be of very little use without my shoulders. Oh, how I wish I could shut up like a telescope! I think I could, if I only knew how to begin."

There seemed to be no use in waiting by the little door, so she went back to the table, half hoping she might find another key on it, or at any rate a book of rules for shutting people up like telescopes: this time she found a little bottle on it ("which certainly was not here before," said Alice), and tied round the neck of the bottle was a paper label with the words "DRINK ME" beautifully printed on it in large letters.

It was all very well to say "Drink me," but the wise little Alice was not going to do *that* in a hurry. "No, I'll look first," she said, "and see whether it's marked 'poison' or not," for she had read several nice little stories about children who had got burnt, and eaten up by wild beasts, and other unpleasant things, all because they *would* not remember the simple rules their friends had taught them, such as, that a red-hot poker will burn you if you hold it too long; and that if you cut your finger *very* deeply with a knife it usually bleeds; and she had never forgotten that if you

---

poker—*a stick used to stir hot coals in a fireplace*

drink much from a bottle marked "poison," it is almost certain to disagree with you sooner or later.

However, the bottle was *not* marked "poison," so Alice ventured to taste it, and finding it very nice (it had, in fact, a sort of mixed flavor of cherry tart, custard, pineapple, roast turkey, toffy, and hot buttered toast), she very soon finished it off.

"What a curious feeling!" said Alice. "I must be shutting up like a telescope."

And so it was, indeed; she was now only ten inches high, and her face brightened up at the thought that she was now the right size for going through the little door into that lovely garden. First, however, she waited for a few minutes to see if she was going to shrink any further; she felt a little nervous about this, "for it might end, you know," said Alice to herself, "in my going out altogether, like a candle."

After a while, finding that nothing more happened, she decided on going into the garden at once; but, alas for poor Alice! when she got to the door, she found she had forgotten the little golden key, and when she went back to the table for it, she found she could not possibly reach it. She could see quite plainly through the glass, and she tried her best to climb up one of the legs of the

---

custard—*a dessert made*
of eggs and milk

toffy—*a chewy candy*

table, but it was too slippery, and when she had tired herself out with trying, the poor little thing sat down and cried.

"Come, there's no use in crying like that!" said Alice to herself rather sharply; "I advise you to leave off this minute!"

Soon her eye fell on a little glass box that was lying under the table: she opened it, and found in it a very small cake, on which the words "EAT ME" were beautifully marked in currants. "Well, I'll eat it," said Alice, "and if it makes me grow larger, I can reach the key; and if it makes me grow smaller, I can creep under the door; so either way I'll get into the garden, and I don't care which hap-pens!"

leave off—*to stop*   currants—*small berries*

She ate a little bit, and said anxiously to herself, "Which way? Which way?" holding her hand on the top of her head to feel which way it was growing, and she was quite surprised to find that she remained the same size.

So she set to work, and very soon finished off the cake.

Will Alice ever find her way through the small door? You will have to read *Alice in Wonderland* to find out.

Thinking It Through

1. What surprising thing did Alice see while sitting on the bank one afternoon?

2. How could you tell that Alice wasn't falling down an ordinary well?

3. Why couldn't Alice go through the passage to the garden?

4. What did Alice do before she drank the bottle marked "Drink me"?

5. When Alice shrank in size, was she able to go through the passage to the garden? What new problem did she have?

About
Elizabeth Eliza's
Piano

Selections from *The Peterkin Papers*
Lucretia P. Hale

The Peterkins lived in the 1800s; they were a loving family, but not always wise. In fact, they would have been quite helpless at times without the advice of the wonderful lady from Philadelphia.

Elizabeth Eliza was given a piano, and she was to take lessons from the postmaster's daughter. They decided to have the piano set across the window in the parlor, and the movers brought it in and went away.

After they had gone, the family all came in to look at the piano; but they found the movers had placed it with its back turned toward the middle of the room, standing close against the window.

How could Elizabeth Eliza open it? How could she reach the keys to play upon it?

Solomon John proposed that they should open the window, which Agamemnon could do

---

Philadelphia (fĭl′ə·dĕl′fē·ə)
postmaster—*the person in charge of a post office*

Agamemnon (ăg′ə·mĕm′nän)

with his long arms. Then Elizabeth Eliza should
go round upon the porch, and open the piano.
Then she could have her music stool on the porch
and play upon the piano there.

So they tried this; and they all thought it was
a very pretty sight to see Elizabeth Eliza playing
the piano while she sat on the porch, with the
honeysuckle vines behind her.

It was very pleasant, too, moonlight evenings.
Mr. Peterkin liked to take a doze on his sofa in

honeysuckle—*a sweet-smelling, flowering plant*

the room; but the rest of the family liked to sit on the porch. So did Elizabeth Eliza, only she had to have her back to the moon.

All this did very well through the summer but when the fall came, Mr. Peterkin thought the air was too cold from the open window, and the family did not want to sit out on the porch.

Elizabeth Eliza practiced in the mornings with her cloak on, but she was obliged to give up her music in the evenings, the family shivered so.

One day, when she was talking with the lady from Philadelphia, she spoke of this trouble.

The lady from Philadelphia looked surprised, and then said, "But why don't you turn the piano around?"

One of the little boys pertly said, "It is a square piano."

But Elizabeth Eliza went home directly, and, with the help of Agamemnon and Solomon John, turned the piano round.

"Why did we not think of that before?" said Mrs. Peterkin. "What shall we do when the lady from Philadelphia goes home again?"

Solomon John Goes For Apples

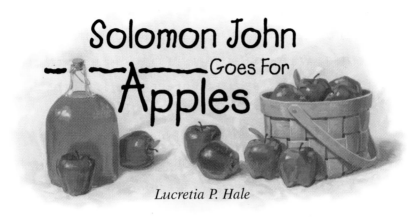

Lucretia P. Hale

Solomon John agreed to ride to Farmer Jones's for a basket of apples, and he decided to go on horseback. The horse was brought round to the door. Now, he had not ridden for a great while, and, though the little boys were there to help him, he had great trouble in getting on the horse.

He tried a great many times, but always found himself facing the wrong way, looking at the horse's tail. They turned the horse's head, first up the street, then down the street; it made no difference; he always made some mistake, and found himself sitting the wrong way.

"Well," said he at last, "I don't know as I care. If the horse has his head in the right direction, that is the main thing. I can turn my head easily enough, to see where we are going." So off he went, and the little boys said he looked like a circus rider, and they were much pleased.

He rode along out of the village, under the elms, very quietly. Pretty soon he came to a bridge, where the road went across a little stream. There was a road at the side, leading down to the stream, because sometimes wagoners watered their horses there. Solomon John's horse turned off, too, to drink some water.

"Very well," said Solomon John, "I don't blame him for wanting to wet his feet and take a drink, this hot day."

When they reached the middle of the stream, the horse bent over his head.

"How far his neck comes into his back!" exclaimed Solomon John; and at that very moment he found he had slid down over the horse's head, and was sitting on a stone, looking into the horse's face. There were two frogs, one on each side of him, sitting just as he was, which pleased Solomon John, so he began to laugh instead of to cry. But the two frogs jumped into the water.

"It is time for me to go on," said Solomon John. So he gave a jump, as he had seen the frogs do; and this time he came all right on the horse's back, facing the way he was going.

"It is a little pleasanter," said he.

---

elm—*a tall shade tree*
wagoner—*a person who drives a wagon*

The horse wanted to nibble a little of the
grass by the side of the way, but Solomon John
remembered what a long neck he had and would
not let him stop.

At last he reached Farmer Jones, who gave
him his basket of apples.

Next he was to go on to a cider mill, up a
little lane by Farmer Jones's house, to get a jug of
cider. But as soon as the horse was turned into
the lane, he began to walk very slowly—so slowly

that Solomon John thought he would not get there before night. He whistled and shouted, and thrust his knees into the horse, but still he would not go.

"Perhaps the apples are too heavy for him," said he. So he began by throwing one of the apples out of the basket. It hit the fence by the side of the road, and that started up the horse and he went on merrily.

"That was the trouble," said Solomon John; "that apple was too heavy for him."

But very soon the horse began to go slower and slower.

So Solomon John thought he would try another apple. This hit a large rock and bounded back under the horse's feet and sent him off at a great pace. But very soon he fell again into a slow walk.

Solomon John had to try another apple. This time it fell into a pool of water and made a great splash, and set the horse off again for a little while; he soon returned to a slow walk—so slow that Solomon John thought it would be tomorrow morning before he got to the cider mill.

"It is rather a waste of apples," thought he; "but I can pick them up as I come back, because the horse will be going home at a quick pace."

So he flung out another apple; that fell among a party of ducks, and they began to make such a quacking and a waddling that it frightened the horse into a quick trot.

So the only way Solomon John could make his horse go was by flinging his apples, now on one side, now on the other. One time he frightened a cow that ran along by the side of the road while the horse raced with her. Another time he started up a brood of turkeys that gobbled and strutted enough to startle twenty horses. In another place he came near hitting a boy, who gave such a scream that it sent the horse off at a furious rate.

And Solomon John got quite excited himself, and he did not stop till he had thrown away all his apples and had reached the corner of the cider mill.

"Very well," said he, "if the horse is so lazy, he won't mind my stopping to pick up the apples on the way home. And I am not sure but I shall prefer walking a little to riding the beast."

The man came out to meet him from the cider mill and gave him the jug. He was just going to take it, when he turned his horse's head round, and, delighted at the idea of going home, the horse set off at a full run without waiting for the jug. Solomon John clung to the reins, and his knees held fast to the horse. He called out "Whoa! whoa!" but the horse would not stop.

He went galloping on past the boy, who stopped and flung an apple at him; past the turkeys, that came and gobbled at him; by the cow, that turned and ran back in a race with them until her breath gave out; by the ducks, that came and quacked at him; by an old donkey, that brayed over the wall at him; by some hens, that ran into the road under the horse's feet and clucked at him; by a great rooster, that stood up on a fence and crowed at him; by Farmer Jones, who looked out to see what had become of him down the village street, and he never stopped till he had reached the door of the house.

Out came Mr. and Mrs. Peterkin, Agamemnon, Elizabeth Eliza, and the little boys.

Solomon John got off his horse all out of breath.

"Where is the jug of cider?" asked Mrs. Peterkin.

"It is at the cider mill," said Solomon John.

"At the mill!" exclaimed Mrs. Peterkin.

"Yes," said Solomon John; "the little boys had better walk out for it; they will enjoy it; and they had better take a basket, for on the way they will find plenty of apples scattered all along either side of the lane, and hens, and ducks, and turkeys, and a donkey."

The little boys looked at each other, and went; but they stopped first, and put on their India-rubber boots.

India-rubber—*crude, natural rubber*

Character Theme—Common Sense

Thinking It Through

1. Why did the piano face the window instead of the parlor?

2. What solution did the Peterkins find for the problem during the summer months?

3. Was this a good solution to the problem? Why or why not?

4. Why do you think Solomon John's horse started going again when he threw out the apples?

5. Why didn't Solomon John get the jug of cider?

6. What kind of sense did the Peterkin family seem to lack?

A Narrow Escape

from *Stuart Little*
E. B. White

> Stuart Little, a mouse, lives in an apartment
> in New York with his parents, and his brother
> George, and a cat named Snowbell. A lovely
> bird named Margalo sleeps in a Boston fern
> in the living room.

Margalo liked it so well at the Littles' house
she decided to stay for a while instead of return-
ing to the open country. She and Stuart became
fast friends, and as the days passed it seemed to
Stuart that she grew more and more beautiful.
He hoped she would never go away from him.

One day when Stuart had recovered from
bronchitis he took his new skates and put on his
ski pants and went out to look for an ice pond.
He didn't get far. The minute he stepped out

Margalo (mär′gə·lō)
bronchitis—*an illness caused by
infection in the bronchial tubes*

into the street he saw an Irish terrier, so he had
to shinny up an iron gate and jump into a garbage can, where he hid in a grove of celery.

While he was there, waiting for the dog to
go away, a garbage truck from the Department
of Sanitation drove up to the curb and two men
picked up the can. Stuart felt himself being
hoisted high in the air. He peered over the side
and saw that in another instant he and everything
in the can would be dumped into the big truck.

"If I jump now I'll kill myself," thought Stuart. So he ducked back into the can and waited.
The men threw the can with a loud bump into
the truck, where another man grabbed it, turned
it upside down, and shook everything out. Stuart
landed on his head, buried two feet deep in wet
slippery garbage. All around him was garbage,
smelling strong. Under him, over him, on all four
sides of him—garbage. Just an enormous world
of garbage and trash and smell. It was a messy
spot to be in. He had egg on his trousers, butter
on his cap, gravy on his shirt, orange pulp in his
ear, and banana peel wrapped around his waist.

Still hanging on to his skates, Stuart tried to
make his way up to the surface of the garbage,

---

terrier—*a type of dog*   sanitation—*waste disposal*
shinny—*climb up using*
  both hands and legs

but the footing was bad. He
climbed a pile of coffee
grounds, but near
the top the grounds
gave way under him
and he slid down and
landed in a pool of
leftover rice pudding.

"I bet I'm going to be sick at my stomach before I get out of this," said Stuart.

He was anxious to work his way up to the
top of the pile because he was afraid of being
squashed by the next can-load of garbage. When
at last he did succeed in getting to the surface,
tired and smelly, he observed that the truck was
not making any more collections but was rum-
bling rapidly along. Stuart glanced up at the sun.
"We're going east," he said to himself. "I wonder
what that means."

There was no way for him to get out of the
truck, the sides were too high. He just had to wait.

When the truck arrived at the East River,
which borders New York City on the east and
which is a rather dirty but useful river, the driver
drove out onto the pier, backed up to a garbage
scow, and dumped his load. Stuart went crashing

---

scow—*a large, flat-bottomed boat*

and slithering along with every-
thing else and hit his head so
hard he fainted and lay quite
still, as though dead. He lay
that way for almost an hour,
and when he recovered his
senses he looked about him and saw nothing but
water. The scow was being towed out to sea.

"Well," thought Stuart, "this is about the worst
thing that could happen to anybody. I guess this
will be my last ride in *this* world." For he knew
that the garbage would be towed twenty miles out
and dumped into the Atlantic Ocean. "I guess
there's nothing I can do about it," he thought,
hopelessly. "I'll just have to sit here bravely and
die like a man. But I wish I didn't have to die with
egg on my pants and butter on my cap and gravy
on my shirt and orange pulp in my ear and banana
peel wrapped around my middle."

The thought of death made Stuart sad, and he
began to think of his home and of his father and
mother and brother and of Margalo and Snowbell
and of how he loved them (all but Snowbell) and
of what a pleasant place his home was, specially

209

in the early morning with the light just coming in through the curtains and the household stirring and waking. The tears came into his eyes when he realized that he would never see them again. He was still sobbing when a small voice behind him whispered:

"Stuart!"

He looked around, through his tears, and there, sitting on a Brussels sprout, was Margalo.

"Margalo!" cried Stuart. "How did *you* get here?"

"Well," said the bird, "I was looking out the window this morning when you left home and I happened to see you get dumped into the garbage truck, so I flew out the window and followed the truck, thinking you might need help."

"I've never been so glad to see anybody in all my life," said Stuart. "But how are you going to help me?"

"I think that if you'll hang on to my feet," said Margalo, "I can fly ashore with you. It's worth trying anyway. How much do you weigh?"

"Three ounces and a half," said Stuart.

"With your clothes on?" asked Margalo.

"Certainly," replied Stuart, modestly.

"Then I believe I can carry you all right."

---

modestly—*done in a proper or humble manner*

"Suppose I get dizzy," said Stuart.

"Don't look down," replied Margalo. "Then you won't get dizzy."

"Suppose I get sick at my stomach."

"You'll just have to *be* sick," the bird replied. "Anything is better than death."

"Yes, that's true," Stuart agreed.

"Hang on, then! We may as well get started."

Stuart tucked his skates into his shirt, stepped gingerly onto a tuft of lettuce, and took a firm grip on Margalo's ankles. "All ready!" he cried.

With a flutter of wings, Margalo rose into the sky, carrying Stuart along, and together they flew out over the ocean and headed toward home.

"Pew!" said Margalo, when they were high in the air, "you smell awful, Stuart."

"I know I do," he replied gloomily. "I hope it isn't making you feel bad."

"I can hardly breathe," she answered. "And my heart is pounding in my breast. Isn't there something you could drop to make yourself lighter?"

"Well, I could drop these ice skates," said Stuart.

"Goodness me," the little bird cried, "I didn't know you had skates hidden in your shirt. Toss those heavy skates away quickly or we will both come down in the ocean and perish." Stuart threw his skates away and watched them fall down, down, till they disappeared in the gray waves below. "That's better," said Margalo. "Now we're all right. I can already see the towers and chimneys of New York."

Fifteen minutes later, in they flew through the open window of the Littles' living room and landed on the Boston fern. Mrs. Little, who had left the window up when she missed Margalo, was glad to see them back, for she was beginning to worry. When she heard what had happened and how near she had come to losing her son, she took Stuart in her hand, even though his clothes smelled nasty, and kissed him. Then she sent him upstairs to take a bath, and sent George out to take Stuart's clothes to the cleaner.

"What was it like, out there in the Atlantic Ocean?" inquired Mr. Little, who had never been very far from home.

So Stuart and Margalo told all about the ocean, and the gray waves curling with white crests, and the gulls in the sky, and the channel buoys and the ships and the tugs and the wind making a sound in your ears. Mr. Little sighed and

---

buoy—*a floating object anchored in a river, etc., to warn of rocks or other danger*

said some day he hoped to get away from business long enough to see all those fine things.

Everyone thanked Margalo for saving Stuart's life; and at suppertime Mrs. Little presented her with a tiny cake, which had seeds sprinkled on top.

You will want to read E. B. White's classic book, *Stuart Little*, for further adventures of this famous mouse.

Character Theme—Friendship, Helpfulness, & Perseverance

Thinking It Through

1. Why was Stuart Little in the garbage can?
2. Where did the garbage truck dump Stuart Little and the garbage?
3. How did Margalo happen to be flying above the scow?
4. How did Margalo rescue him?
5. What extra weight did Margalo ask Stuart Little to drop?

Sequoya:
The Cherokee Who Captured Words

Lillie Patterson

Sequoya sang a Song for Thinking. As he sang, he slowly scratched a picture of a horse on a stone.

"*Ha-ya!*" he sang out. "I will draw our Cherokee language. I will make a picture for every word we speak."

Still singing, he limped to the forest. A sickness in his childhood had left one leg weaker and shorter than the other, but that did not keep him from being a hard worker and thinker.

He began to cut thin strips of bark from birch trees. All the while he sang a Song for Starting New Things.

Working beside his house, Sequoya drew pictures on the smooth inside of the bark strips. Little Ah-yoka, his daughter, came to look on with

---

Sequoya (sĭ·kwoi′ə)
Cherokee (chĕr′ə·kē)

Ah-yoka (ä′yō′kə)

214

wide eyes. She picked up a bark picture. "This is a house."

"Yes, Little One," Sequoya said. "Each picture will show a different word. Look! This is for the word *pot*. This is for *fox*. And this is for *fish*."

When cold weather came, Sequoya took his drawings indoors. Ah-yoka sat beside her father and kept him company. She seemed to know that he was doing something very important.

The pile of bark grew higher. There were thousands of words in the Cherokee language. Each word stood for at least one thing or idea. Sequoya faced several hard problems. A picture of a girl could stand for Ah-yoka. But it could stand for other little girls as well. "How can I show the difference?" Sequoya wondered.

Many words could not be made into pictures. "How can I show words such as *good* or *bad?*" Sequoya wondered aloud. "What can I use for *today* or *tomorrow?*"

In time, he hit upon a new plan. He began to make up symbols, or signs, for different words. But soon he had so many symbols, he could not remember which one stood for which word. If he forgot, how could other people remember?

His friends could not understand the change in Sequoya. One day a man named Turtle Fields came to see him. "My good friend, our people grow more worried about you," Turtle Fields said. "They think you are wasting your life."

Sequoya answered in a soft voice. "Tell our people that what I am doing will be of help to every Cherokee. Tell our people that I shall go on."

One morning Sequoya sat thinking. "There must be a better way," he said aloud. "I can never make enough signs for every Cherokee word. Never!"

A few days later, Sequoya came across something that gave him new ideas. He found a child's spelling book beside a road. A teacher, sent by a church, had opened a school nearby for Cherokee children.

He took the speller home and began to study it. He had no idea what the names of the letters were or what each meant. Day after day he looked at the black marks printed in rows.

"See," he showed them to Ah-yoka. "The same marks are put down again and again." He counted them. "Yes, there are 26 of the strange shapes. The whole book is made up of only 26 different signs." Of course, Sequoya was looking at the letters of our alphabet, *a* to *z*.

He began to draw each of the letters. He liked the way they looked. They could be made with simple lines and curves. "Perhaps I can use some of them for my own signs," Sequoya said.

Late one night he sat studying the speller. A pine log burning in the fireplace gave him light. Suddenly the answer came to him. "Sounds!" he cried out. "Each sign is for a different sound. Put together, the sounds make words."

Next morning he got a fresh bundle of bark. "This time I know I am on the right track," he told Ah-yoka.

"What will you do now?" Ah-yoka asked.

"*Ha-ya!*" Sequoya swung her high into the air. "I do not need a different sign for every single word. I can break our Cherokee words into parts. All I need is a sign for the sound each part makes."

"Oh, can I help?" Ah-yoka asked.

"Indeed, you can," Sequoya answered. "You are young, but you think quickly. You have keen ears and sharp eyes."

Sequoya began to draw. "Sequoya," he sang his name. "Se-quoy-a. It has three parts. I can make a sign for each. When I put the three signs together, they will show my whole name."

"Can you show my name?" Ah-yoka wanted to know.

"Ah-yo-ka," sang the Lame One. "Ah. The

first part of your name is like the last part of mine. They will take the same sign. I can use the same symbols for the same sounds in different words."

"How many signs will you need?" Ah-yoka asked.

Sequoya tried to find the answer in the months that followed. He tried to remember all the words he had ever said or heard. He broke each word into parts, or syllables—"Hee-tun-hah-yu-hoo." He said each syllable while Ah-yoka listened. Then she sounded words for him to hear.

He was working on a way of writing called a syllabary. It is like an alphabet, yet different. An alphabet has a sign for any one of the tiny sounds that make up a word. Each letter stands alone. A syllabary has a sign for each spoken syllable. For example, an important city in Tennessee has the Cherokee name, Chat-ta-noo-ga. It is spelled with eleven letters of the alphabet. It is written with only four of Sequoya's symbols, or letters.

Sequoya counted 100 of these big sounds, or syllables, in the Cherokee language. After that he decided on a symbol to match each one.

Sequoya knew that some members of the Cherokee Nation had moved beyond the Mississippi River. "We will go far away and build a new home," he told Ah-yoka one day in 1818.

Later, Ah-yoka sat atop a roll of blankets in a big, flat-bottomed boat. "We are on our way West," she sang.

Sequoya smiled at the happy seven-year-old.

For weeks the boats followed the small rivers into the great rivers. Every day Sequoya studied his signs.

Ah-yoka found the trip exciting. She made friends with a woman named Sally and her son,

---

syllabary—*a set of signs representing syllables of a language*

Squirrel Boy, who was eight years old. Squirrel Boy's father was dead.

Sally and Sequoya became great friends, too, and were soon married.

They reached Arkansas in spring. The happy family worked together to make a home in the wild country. Sequoya cut trees and split logs for the new house. He cleared land, and the children helped to plant a garden. He built roads. At times his lame leg hurt so he could hardly walk.

The next year was not so hard. Sequoya set up a trading post. There he met many people. He listened carefully to the words they spoke. "Say that word again," he would ask strangers. If he heard a new word sound, he made a sign for it.

Sequoya worked on his word signs at night. "They must be easy to make and easy to learn," he told his family. After a year of hard work, he found that he needed only 86 signs, not 100. Any Cherokee word could be written by using one or more of them.

Sequoya picked out the 86 symbols he liked best. He kept many letters of the alphabet, but changed them to his liking. He drew some upside down, others sideways or backward. Sometimes he added little squiggles and fancy lines.

Cherokee Alphabet

D	R	T	Ꮝ	Ꮻ	i
Ꮎ Ꮣ	Ᏼ	Ꭹ	A	J	E
Ꮕ	Ꮖ	Ꭷ	Ꮖ	Ꮁ	Ꮇ
W	Ꮳ	Ꮑ	Ꮐ	M	Ꮃ
Ꮜ	Ꮅ	H	Ꮒ	Ᏺ	
Ꮎ Ꮏ Ꮐ	Ꮩ	h	Z	Ꮑ	Ꮞ
Ꮚ	Ꮣ	Ꮖ	Ꮗ	Ꮼ Ꮛ	
Ꮖ Ꮚ	Ꮞ	Ꮔ	ᏔꞮ	Ᏽ R	
Ꮬ W	Ꮆ Ꮏ	Ꮷ Ꮲ	Ꮜ	S Ꮝ	
Ꮿ Ꮑ	L	C	Ꮻ	Ꮛ P	
Ꮆ	Ꮴ	Ꮒ	K	Ꮷ Ꮯ	
Ꮐ	Ꮗ	Ꮎ	Ꮳ	Ꮆ 6	
Ꮬ	ᏸ	Ꮬ	Ꮧ	Ꮐ B	

He wanted each symbol to express meaning
and feeling. At last his 86 signs, or letters, were
ready.

"Now they must be taught to others," Sequoya said. "My family will be my first students."

Ah-yoka already knew the signs. She helped
to teach Sally and Squirrel Boy.

Every evening the family sat around a table near the stone fireplace. One person would call out a word. The others wrote it. Soon they began to write sentences.

"Writing is as easy as playing a game," wrote Squirrel Boy one night.

Sequoya was happy. His writing signs were easy to learn. After twelve years of hard work, he had captured Cherokee words on paper. His dream had come true.

Sequoya wanted to teach his writing to everyone in the Cherokee Nation. "I will get permission from the leading chiefs," he told his family. "I must go back East."

"Please take me," Ah-yoka cried excitedly.

Sequoya hugged his ten-year-old daughter. "You have been my helper all along. You should go with me now."

At last, Sequoya stood before the Cherokee Tribal Council. It was 1821. He held up a deerskin with his 86 letters. "This is my gift to our people," he began. "Please let me teach these signs to you and to everyone."

He went on to tell the importance of a written language. "We could print our own books and newspapers. We could open schools. . . ." On and on he talked.

"Ha!" One chief spoke up. "Your black marks look like bird tracks on snow. Can you really write words with them?"

"Is this a trick?" asked another chief. "You were always good at telling stories."

John Ross, the council leader, held up his hand. "Will you let us test you, Sequoya?"

"Yes," Sequoyah said readily. "I will leave the room. My daughter will take my place. Speak to her, and she will write down what you say. When I come back, I will read what she has written."

John Ross led Ah-yoka into the room. She sat down at a table. Her hands shook a little as she picked up a piece of paper. Then she took a deep breath and looked straight at the chiefs.

One of them said a few words. Ah-yoka began writing. Another chief spoke, then another. Ah-yoka wrote their words.

When Sequoya came back, she handed him the paper. He saw at once that she had set down the words in neat rows. Aloud he read back what she had written.

"Ho! Ho!" the chiefs cried in wonder. "Can this be true?" Some still did not believe.

"We will have another test," Sequoya said. "This time Ah-yoka will leave. I will write what you say."

That is how it went. The chiefs
talked, and Sequoya wrote what they
said. Ah-yoka came back and read what
he had written.

"It is true!" the chiefs shouted. "They are
talking on paper."

At last they believed Sequoya. "We will send
young men to you," they said. "If you can teach
them, you may teach everyone."

The young men learned the signs in a short
time. After that the chiefs gave a great feast to
honor the Lame One.

Word of the great gift spread quickly. An
amazing thing happened. Old and young came to
learn how to talk on paper.

Men left their hunting and farming. Women

left their spinning and came with babies on their backs. The children were more excited than their mothers and fathers. They left their playthings to learn the new game of reading and writing. It was more fun than a corn festival. It was more exciting than a ball game in spring.

The Cherokees wrote with whatever they had— sticks, knives, charcoal, brushes, and pens made from turkey feathers. The 86 letters could be seen printed on fences and door-steps. They were cut into wayside trees or written in the dust of roadways. They covered the walls of homes.

"Teach everyone you meet," Sequoya told his tribe. "Turn your villages into schoolrooms."

The people did as he said. They taught one another in homes, in fields, under trees, and beside rivers. The Cherokees learned to read and write without money, books, or schools.

Sequoya stayed with the Eastern Cherokees for a year. Then father and daughter went back to teach Indians in the West.

Sequoya asked no pay for his work. He looked upon it as a gift to his people. "It is a great gift," many said. "It is worth more than a bag of gold to every Cherokee."

Sequoya spent the next years training teachers and opening schools. Thanks to him, and to his syllabary, the Cherokees made great progress. They set up their own printing press. Every year they printed school books, Bibles, and magazines.

A newspaper, the *Cherokee Phoenix,* came out every week. It printed the new Cherokee Constitution and the facts about laws and treaties. People could read about their customs, celebrations, weddings, and other events.

Sequoya loved words, and words have kept his name and spirit alive. A county in Oklahoma is named for him. In other states his name has been given to mountains, streets, and societies. He is honored by statues, markers, and monuments.

Perhaps the greatest monuments are the giant sequoia trees in California. The oldest and tallest trees in America, they tower hundreds of feet toward the sky. The land where they grow is named Sequoia National Park. These magnificent evergreens stand as a symbol of the courage and greatness of the Lame One.

His name may be spelled *Sequoia* or *Sequoya* or *Sequoyah*. However it is spelled, the name is a beautiful one to remember.

Character Theme—Industry, Purpose, & Perseverance

Thinking It Through

1. What did Sequoya want to do for his people?
2. Who was Sequoya's faithful helper?
3. What did Sequoya draw his pictures on?
4. When did Sequoya realize that drawing a symbol or sign for each word in his language would not work?
5. What did each of the symbols that Sequoya later developed stand for?
6. What is Sequoya's way of writing called?
7. How did Sequoya convince the Cherokee Tribal Council to let him teach his writing to their people?

Charles Roman:

A Doctor of Medicine

L. H. Hammond

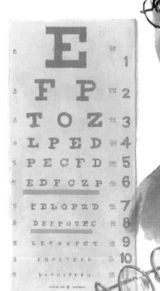

Twenty years or so before the Civil War, a Maryland slave ran away from his master and went to Canada by the "underground railway." That was the name for the chain of homes and stopping-places where blacks fleeing from slavery were hidden and cared for by those who sympathized with them. If slaves were discovered before they got out of the United

States, the law required sheriffs and policemen, even in the free states, to arrest them and return them to their masters; but if they got across the line into Canada, they could not be brought back. Quakers and others who thought that slavery was wrong arranged stopping-places all the way up to Canada, and many slaves made their way along these routes to freedom.

This Maryland slave, named Roman, was passed on from hiding-place to hiding-place until at last he reached Ontario, in Canada, and there he lived and worked for over twenty years. He married the daughter of a black farmer who had run away from Virginia long years before.

When Lincoln's proclamation freeing the slaves made it safe to return to the United States, Roman took his family to Williamsport, Pennsylvania, and there, on the 4th of July, 1864, his son Charles was born.

The family was large, and they knew what it was to be poor and without many of the comforts of life. Sometimes, however, people who do without comfort get something bigger and better in its place; they learn to be brave and cheerful no matter what their surroundings are. Young Charles

---

proclamation—*something that is announced officially*

Roman was one of these fortunate people. The hard lessons he mastered helped him during the struggle of his early years and gave him a quick sympathy for others who struggled. Much of his happiness in life would come from giving to others the help he himself used to need so much.

Charles liked to discover things for himself. A little brook ran near his home, and he wanted to find out where it came from. When he was a tiny child, only three or four years old, he set out to find the beginning of that brook. He walked a great distance and was gone so long that his mother roused the neighborhood to help her find him. They searched the fields and the woods, and at last they found the boy at the place where the brook began—a little pool with a bubbling spring at the bottom of it. He was watching it as hard as he could, more puzzled than ever as to where the water came from and still determined to find out. But his mother carried him off home, and if he had intended trying to get down the hole at the bottom of the pool, his plans were nipped in the bud.

When Charles was six years old, the family went back to Canada, and until he was twelve, the boy spent much of his time on his grandfather's

---

roused—*called to get help*

farm. He had all sorts of adventures here. He tried to ride the steers like the big boys and was tossed over the fence. He would walk a mile to the pasture gate to open it for his grandfather so that he might ride back with him as a reward. He climbed the fruit trees to eat all one boy could possibly hold, trotted after the sheep, and often got into mischief which tried his grandmother's patience.

But play-days were soon over. In those days, children often had to work all day to help their families. When Charles was twelve years old, his parents moved to Dundas, Ontario, and Charles went to work in a cotton mill.

The machinery started at six o'clock, and any-one who was not at the mill ten minutes before-hand had to go to the office for discipline. This was such an unpleasant experience that most of the boys arrived far ahead of time. Charlie Roman put himself on the safe side by being on hand every morning at half-past five.

With work lasting for ten and a half hours, there was little time left for other things. But the boy's heart was set on having an education. There were so many things he wanted to find out that he spent two hours every evening at night-school,

---

machinery—*the working parts of a machine*

studying afterwards at home until far into the night. He read every book he could lay his hands on, borrowing them wherever he could.

On Sundays he went regularly to Sunday school and studied his Bible as far as his opportunities made possible. Charlie belonged to a little band of people who promised never to touch strong drink. And behind everything he did, this boy had one settled purpose in life.

One day at the noon hour the boys at the mill were telling each other what they planned to be when they grew up. Charles, the one black boy in the group, and a white boy named Arthur, were the only two who had nothing to say. After a while, one of the bigger boys turned to shy Arthur in a bullying, sneering way and asked, "Well, Arthur, what are you going to be?"

"I'm going to be a musician," replied the boy, quietly.

A howl of derision went up at this. They looked at him, poorly clad, without money or friends, tied to a factory ten hours a day for barely enough to keep himself alive, and they laughed until they nearly lost their breath.

When the delightful edge of the joke was

---

derision—*ridicule; mocking laughter*

dulled a little, the big boy turned to the silent black boy, sneering more than ever. "And what are *you* going to be, if you please?" he inquired.

"A doctor of medicine," came the answer, quick as a flash.

How they roared at that! They laughed until they almost cried, and went back to work at last still chuckling and thinking the big boy who had asked the questions a very master of humor.

But both those boys told the truth. Arthur became the leader of an orchestra, and Charles did indeed become a medical doctor.

Charles worked in the mill for five years— until he was seventeen years old. All this time he studied and read at night, and all this time his thirst for knowledge grew. Then came an accident at the mill which sent him to the hospital badly hurt. He was there a long time. One operation after another was performed, and for months the boy fought for his life through suffering and almost despair.

When at last he came out of the hospital, he was on crutches, lame for life. To such a big, strong, active young fellow, this must have been a great trial. It was well that he had developed a strong Christian faith, for he needed all the comfort it could give him.

But often, through the very troubles which seem to block our way, God opens a door through which we pass to something even better than our dreams. Now that Charles was hopelessly disqualified as a mill worker, it was decided that he must have a chance at the brain work he so wanted. On crutches, therefore, he started his schooling in nearby Hamilton, Ontario. He worked as hard as though lameness did not exist, finishing the six years' course in three.

Before school and after, Charles found time to help pay his way through school. He sold notions, such as needles and thread, wherever he could find a buyer and did all the odd jobs possible to one in his condition. Despite his drawbacks, the young man was so brave and cheerful that he made friends for himself everywhere he went, among both white and black people.

"I have taught hundreds of boys," said one of his teachers years afterward, "but among them all this boy had the brightest mind I ever touched."

234

After graduation, Charles went south, feeling that there he could best serve his people. He taught school in Kentucky, then in Tennessee, and at length in Nashville, the capital.

Meharry College, the best medical school for blacks in the South, was in Nashville. Charles Roman was anxious to enter the college at once, but could not for lack of money. However, while teaching in the public schools, he began to study the books in the medical course. As soon as he had saved enough money, he entered Meharry as a regular student. He worked during vacations in a black physician's office and finished his course with honor.

After working briefly as a doctor in Tennessee, Dr. Roman went to Dallas, Texas, where he built up a successful practice. He was still a student by nature, and from time to time took post-graduate courses in Chicago and Philadelphia. Then he went to schools in London and Paris, specializing in diseases of the eye, ear, nose, and throat. On his return from Europe, he became a professor at Meharry. He traveled all over the country for the United States government during World War I, reaching many thousands of young men of his own race with sound teaching founded both on his knowledge of medicine and his living faith in Jesus Christ.

235

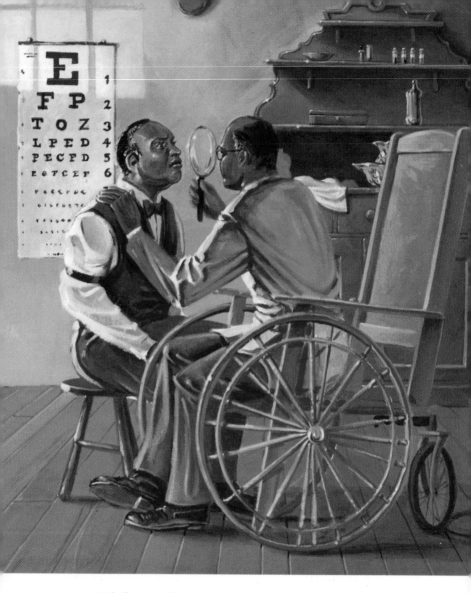

While teaching at Meharry and attending to
his large and growing practice in the city, he still
found time to study, not only to keep up in his
profession, but to broaden his life in other fields.
Several colleges offered him honorary degrees,
but he did not want anything he had not earned.

Professor though he was, he studied at Fisk University, winning his Master of Arts degree in 1913. He was nearly fifty years old at this time, but he knew he would never be too old to learn. Later he became director of physiology and hygiene at Fisk as well as a professor at Meharry.

Dr. Roman was an active worker in his church. Into his Bible class of two hundred young men and women, he put his whole heart. Sunday after Sunday and year after year students crowded into his class.

It was the same with his medical classes. Because of a real love for teaching and for his students, he quickened both their minds and their hearts. They loved him and trusted him, and he helped so many in difficulty and trouble, both outward and inward, that he could not remember the half of it himself. He never forgot his own struggles with poverty, with misunderstanding, with pain, and with discouragement, and he knew how to help and comfort others who were themselves struggling in like manner.

Character Theme—Humility, Industry, & Perseverance

Thinking It Through

1. What was the Underground Railroad?

2. Where did Charles Roman live most of the time he was growing up?

3. How many hours a day did Charles work in the cotton mill?

4. What happened to Charles when he was seventeen that left him lame for the rest of his life?

5. How did Charles pay for his schooling?

6. Why didn't Charles Roman accept honorary degrees that were offered to him?

7. How can you tell that Charles Roman had a real love for learning and teaching?

Good Advice

Adapted from the German
Louis Untermeyer

Don't shirk
Your work
For the sake of a dream;
A fish
In the dish
Is worth ten in the stream.

Motto

Adapted from the German
Louis Untermeyer

However they talk, whatever they say,
Look straight at the task without dismay—
And if you can do it, do it today.

---

shirk—*neglect; avoid*
dismay—*a lack of courage or confidence*

Thomas Jefferson, Esquire *Nan Gilbert*

On the mountain across the river from his home, Master Tom lay staring out over the velvety green valley spread below him.

Tomorrow he must leave all this countryside that he loved and go off to school. And although the school was only two days' journey down the river, it would be another world.

Tom's horse left off cropping the grass to push his nose questioningly against the boy's shoulder. Tom turned his thin face away. Nine-

240

going-on-ten was far too old for tears, so even his horse must not see the dampness in Tom's eyes.

"Arithmetic . . . spelling . . . French," Tom puzzled out loud. "What does a fellow need with all that stuff? It means a lot more to know how to ride and swim and look after the crops!"

But Tom's father had already spoken, and in 1752, a father's word was law for his son. Tom was to enter a private school now, and later he would go to college.

Young though he was, Tom must start living by two of his father's unchangeable rules. "A man must learn to be useful" was one of them. And "Never ask another to do what you can do for yourself" was the other.

"Without an education, you cannot live by either rule," his father had told him. "For without education, you would be neither useful nor able to do things for yourself."

---

unchangeable—*unable to be changed*

"But I can learn the work of the plantation by riding at your side," Tom had suggested eagerly. "I can learn how to look after the corn and wheat and how to raise our cows and sheep and pigs!

"I can learn other things, too—how to grind wheat into flour, shear the sheep for our wool, and cut the trees for our lumber. Surely this is schooling a-plenty, Father!"

"But how would you know whether you had made money on a crop if you could not keep your own accounts?" his father asked. "And how could you welcome the guests from high places who visit our home if you had no command of language or books?"

"*You* could do those things, Father," Tom begged.

But his father shook his head. "You cannot know what lies ahead of you in your life, Tom. Whatever it is, you must be prepared for it in mind as well as in body."

So this was to be Tom's last day of freedom, and during it, he would do all of his favorite things. He had ridden in the fields by the side of his father this morning. He had visited his

---

plantation—*an area for growing crops*
accounts—*business records*

beloved little mountain this afternoon. Now he would catch a string of fish and cook one.

And this evening, the family would all gather around the fireside to sing. Then, later, they would listen to his father's stories of the days when he was a surveyor.

Oh, life on the plantation was such a pleasant, satisfying life! Why did the pattern have to be broken for school?

The fishing was not good that afternoon. Slowly the sun crossed the sky above him and flung long shadows across the fields. But not a single fish had nibbled his bait, though Tom had followed the stream farther than ever before.

Disappointed, he shouldered his pole and his lines and put his horse's reins over his arm.

As Tom rounded the next bend in the stream, he came upon a sandy cove. Smoke was rising from a small campfire. A boy not much older than Tom scrambled to his feet, ready to run for the woods.

"What a fine catch you've made!" cried Tom. "Your luck has certainly been better than mine today—or perhaps you're just a better fisherman!"

---

surveyor—*a person who surveys land*

The shy boy from the backwoods reddened with pleasure. "I've a big one cooking in the ashes," he said. "Take it, and welcome."

"I will, if you will eat it with me," answered Tom.

While they were eating the good browned fish, the boy told Tom that his name was Eb. He lived with his old grandfather, some distance away from Tom's plantation.

Tom, in turn, told about the dreaded schooling that he must start the next day. He glanced toward Eb, expecting to find the boy feeling sorry for him. But, to his surprise, he saw only longing in Eb's eyes.

"Say, I believe *you* would rather go to school than fish!"

"Oh, yes, I would!" cried Eb longingly. "With schooling, I could learn to be a surveyor. That's what I want more than anything."

"Wouldn't your grandfather let you go to school?" asked Tom with curiosity.

Eb shrugged his shoulders hopelessly. "School's not for the poor, Master Tom. Where would Grandpa get the money?"

Tom frowned. He had never thought before about the boys who could not afford to go to a private school or to college. There must be many boys like Eb, who would never be able to do the work they wanted because they couldn't afford to learn.

"But that isn't fair!" he burst out. "Learning ought to be free to anyone who wants it! How's a fellow going to lead a useful life if he can't study what he doesn't know? How's he going to be ready for whatever comes, the way my father says he should be?"

Eb ducked his head shyly. "I wasn't complaining, Master Tom. There are lots of ways for a boy to be useful, even without book-learning."

"Yes," said Tom, "if a fellow's father shears sheep, *he* can shear sheep! And if his father shoes horses, *he* can shoe horses! But what if he wants to be a surveyor, as you want to be? Or what if he wants to keep store, or practice law, or mix medicines?

"People should *want* him to learn, not hold him back! I think going to school should be *free!*"

It was a big idea, bigger than any idea he had had before. He would have to think about it some more, after he got to school. Tom swung up onto his horse and said good-bye to Eb.

shear—*cut wool off a sheep*

Suddenly he felt eager for tomorrow to come. Maybe his father was right. It was high time he got started with his schooling and began to learn some of the many things he did not yet know.

Perhaps he would find out how a person should go about convincing the king's colony of Virginia that its schools should be free. It just wasn't fair that boys like Eb should not have a chance to learn, too.

Tom was fourteen years old when next he came to the sandy cove where he had first talked with Eb. His new black suit made his thin, big-boned figure look even thinner, and his hair even redder.

Today he carried no fishing pole. He had come only to escape the heavy sadness that filled his home. Tom's father was dead.

His father had been big, strong, more powerful than Tom would ever be—yet he was dead. Tom must now take his place as the head of Shadwell, his plantation home.

There was so much to know, so much for him yet to learn! Had this been in his father's mind when he said Tom must be prepared in mind as well as in body for whatever came?

Was this why his father had trained him to usefulness, so he could take over the plantation while he was still but a boy? Or might there be even more ahead that he should be ready for?

Tom knew he could not find answers to these questions now. He must take his father's word for it and prepare, with more schooling, with further reading, with college, for whatever might come. It did not seem as if life could ever hold a bigger job than managing Shadwell—but who could tell?

Thoughtfully, Tom picked up a long stick and began to scratch his name in the sand. Today he was no longer "Master Tom," or "young Tom." Today he took a man's place at Shadwell, and a man's name to go with it. In those days, the word *Esquire* was used after a man's name. With one final, dashing stroke, Tom wrote, for the first time,

"Thomas Jefferson, Esquire."

Tom could not know, the first time he wrote the name Thomas Jefferson, Esquire, how famous his name was going to become, later on. But life had much more responsibility in store for young Tom than the management of the family plantation.

Nowadays, when we think about liberty and justice and freedom, we think with pride of Thomas Jefferson, the third President of the United States. We think of the great American statesman who helped to make liberty and justice and freedom really stand for the American way of life.

Character Theme—Usefulness & Wisdom

Thinking It Through

1. Why was Master Tom so unhappy?
2. Why did Tom's father think that an education was so important?
3. Why wasn't Eb able to go to school when he wanted to go so badly?
4. What big idea did Tom have that day about going to school?
5. How did Tom begin writing his name after his father died?

My Story

Helen Keller

What do you think life would be like for you if you could not see, hear, or speak? How would you know what the world was like? How would you communicate with those around you? When Helen Keller was a baby, she became deaf and blind. Life was very confusing and lonely for her until a teacher came and opened up to her the world of words and the world of love.

Helen was very quick to learn, and when she was 12 years old, in 1892, she wrote an *autobiography,* or story of her own life. It was published in a children's magazine called *Youth's Companion.* The first part of the autobiography is given here as she wrote it, without help of any sort.

Helen Keller became a famous example of how a handicapped person can learn to make use of the gifts God has given and can be of help to others. She was a friend of many of the well-known people of her day, including inventors, Presidents, and writers.

I was born twelve years ago, one bright June morning, in Tuscumbia, a pleasant little town in the northern part of Alabama. The beginning of my life was very simple, and very much like the beginning of every other little life; for I could see and hear when I first came to live in this beautiful world. But I did not notice anything in my new home for several days. Content in my mother's tender arms I lay, and smiled as if my little heart were filled with sweetest memories of the world I had just left.

I like to think I lived with God in the beautiful Somewhere before I came here, and that is why I always knew God loved me, even when I had forgotten His name.

But when I did begin to notice things, my blue eyes were filled with wondering joy. I gazed long at the lonely, deep-blue sky, and stretched out my tiny hands for golden sunbeams that came to play hide-and-seek with me. So my happy baby hours went. I grew and cried and laughed, as all infants do.

In the meantime, I had a name given to me; I was called Helen, because Helen means light, and my mother liked to think that my life would be full of the brightness of the day.

Tuscumbia (tŭs·cŭm′bē·ə)

Of course, my recollections of my early childhood are very indistinct. I have confused memories of long summer days filled with light, and the voices of birds singing in the clear sunshine. I seem to remember, as if it were yesterday, being lost in a great green place, where there were beautiful flowers and fragrant trees.

I stood under one tall plant, and let its blossoms rest upon my curly head. I saw little flakes of light flitting among the flowers; I suppose they were birds, or, perhaps, butterflies.

I discovered the true way to walk the day I was a year old, and, during the radiant summer days that followed, I was never still a minute. My mother watched me coming, going, laughing, playing, prattling, with proud, happy eyes. I was her only child, and she thought there never had been another baby quite so beautiful as her little Helen.

Then, when my father came in the evening, I would run to the gate to meet him, and he would take me up in his strong arms, and put back the tangled

recollections—*memories*
indistinct—*unclear*
radiant—*bright*

prattling—
chattering;
talking a lot

curls from my face and kiss me many times, saying, "What has my Little Woman been doing today?"

But the brightest summer has winter behind it. In the cold, dreary month of February, when I was nineteen months old, I had a serious illness. My mother sat beside my little bed, and tried to soothe my feverish moans, while in her troubled heart she prayed, "Father in Heaven, spare my baby's life!" But the fever grew and flamed in my eyes, and for several days my kind physician thought I would die.

But early one morning the fever left me as mysteriously and unexpectedly as it had come, and I fell into a quiet sleep. Then my parents knew I would live, and they were very happy. They did not know for some time after my recovery that the cruel fever had taken my sight and hearing—taken all the light and music and gladness out of my little life.

By-and-by the sad truth dawned upon them, and the thought that their little daughter would never more see the beautiful light, or hear the voices she loved, filled their hearts with anguish.

But I was too young to realize what had happened. When I awoke and found that all was dark

---

anguish—*pain; distress*

and still, I suppose I thought it was night, and I must have wondered why day was so long coming. Gradually, however, I got used to the silence and darkness that surrounded me, and forgot that it had ever been day.

I forgot everything that had been, except my mother's tender love. Soon even my childish voice was stilled, because I had ceased to hear any sound.

But all was not lost! After all, sight and hearing are but two of the beautiful blessings which God had given me. The most precious, the most wonderful of His gifts was still mine. My mind remained clear and active, "Though fled fore'er the light."

As soon as my strength returned, I began to take an interest in what the people around me were doing. I would cling to my mother's dress as she went about her household duties, and my little hands felt every object and observed every motion, and in this way I learned a great many things.

When I was a little older, I felt the need of some means of communication with those around me, and I began to make simple signs which my parents and friends readily understood; but it often happened that I was unable to express my thoughts intelligently, and at such times I would give way to my angry feelings utterly.

Of course, my parents were very anxious about me when I behaved so ill, and they tried to think of some way of having me educated. Finally, they decided that I must have a teacher.

It was March before my teacher came to me. The fruit trees were blooming, and in the garden the mockingbirds were building their nests anew. Oh, how well I remember the evening when she came! My mother had made me understand in a dim way that a lady was coming who would have something to do with me.

I was standing on the porch when Teacher arrived. I had been waiting there ever since my mother kissed me and went to the station to meet the strange lady.

Suddenly I felt approaching footsteps; they came nearer; I stretched out my little hand eagerly; someone took it, and in another instant I was in my teacher's arms. I felt her face and hands curiously, and let her kiss me, while feelings that I cannot describe entered my heart.

We could not speak to each other; I could not ask her why she had come. Yet I am sure I felt, in a vague, bewildered way, that something beautiful was going to happen to me. I knew the

---

vague—*uncertain; not clearly understood*
bewildered—*confused*

strange lady loved me, and that her love would make my life sweet and good and happy.

The morning after Teacher came, I went to her room, and found her very busy unpacking her trunk; but she did not send me away. She let me stay and help her. When everything was in its place, she kissed me kindly and gave me a beautiful doll. Then Teacher took my hand and slowly made the letters d-o-l-l with her fingers, at the same time making me touch the doll.

Of course, I did not know the motions meant letters. I did not know what letters were; but I was interested in the finger-play, and tried to imitate the motions, and I think I succeeded in spelling "doll" in a very little while. Then I ran downstairs to show my new doll to my mother, and I am sure she was surprised and pleased when I held up my little hand and made the letters for doll.

That afternoon, besides "doll," I learned to spell "pin" and "hat"; but I did not understand that everything had a name. I had not the least idea that my finger-play was the magical key which was to unlock my mind's prison door and open wide the windows of my soul.

Teacher had been with me nearly two weeks, and I had learned eighteen or twenty words, before that thought flashed into my mind, as the sun breaks upon the sleeping world; and in that moment of illumination the secret language was revealed to me, and I caught a glimpse of the beautiful country I was about to explore.

Teacher had been trying all the morning to make me understand that the mug and the milk in the mug had different names; but I was very dull, and kept spelling "milk" for mug and "mug" for milk, until Teacher must have lost all hope of making me see my mistake.

At last she got up, gave me the mug, and led me out of the door to the pump-house. Someone was pumping water, and, as the cool, fresh stream burst forth, Teacher made me put my mug under the spout and spell w-a-t-e-r. Water!

That word startled my soul, and it awoke, full of the spirit of the morning—full of joyous, exultant song. Till that day, my mind had been like a darkened chamber, waiting for words to enter and light the lamp, which is thought.

I left the pump-house eager to learn every-thing. We met the nurse carrying my little sister, and Teacher spelled "baby." For the first time, I

---

illumination—*brightness; light*
pump-house—*a small building where water was pumped from a well*

exultant—*happy; rejoicing*
chamber—*a room*

was impressed with the smallness and helplessness of a little baby, and, mingled with that thought, there was another one of myself, and I was glad I was myself, and not a baby.

I learned a great many words that day. I do not remember what they all were; but I do know that "mother," "father," "sister," and "teacher" were among them. It would have been difficult to find a happier little child than I was that night, as I lay in my crib and thought over the joy the day had brought me, and, for the first time, longed for a new day to come.

The next morning I awoke with joy in my heart. Everything I touched seemed to quiver with life. It was because I saw everything with the new, strange, beautiful sight which had been given me.

I was never angry after that, because I understood what my friends said to me, and I was very busy learning many wonderful things.

I was never still during the first glad days of my freedom. I was continually spelling, and acting out the words as I spelled them.

quiver—*tremble*

I would run, skip, jump, and swing, no matter where I happened to be. Everything was budding and blossoming. The honeysuckle hung in long garlands, deliciously fragrant, and the roses had never been so beautiful before. Teacher and I lived out-of-doors from morning until night, and I rejoiced greatly in the forgotten light and sunshine found again.

Character Theme—Perseverance & Resourcefulness

Thinking It Through

1. How old was Helen Keller when she wrote this story about her life?
2. Why did she become deaf and blind?
3. What did Helen's teacher give her the day she arrived?
4. How did she introduce Helen to words that day?
5. How did the understanding of what words were change Helen's life?

Afternoon on a Hill

Edna St. Vincent Millay

I will be the gladdest thing
Under the sun!
I will touch a hundred flowers
And not pick one.

I will look at cliffs and clouds
With quiet eyes,
Watch the wind bow down the grass,
And the grass rise.

And when the lights begin to show
Up from the town,
I will mark which must be mine,
And then start down!

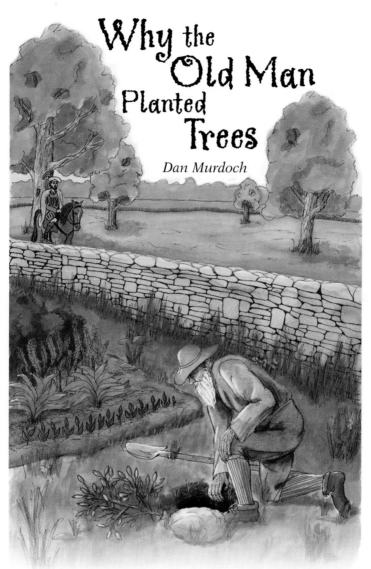

Why the Old Man Planted Trees

Dan Murdoch

A nobleman was once riding along the road
and saw a very old man digging in his garden.
Beside the old man, on the ground, lay a sapling
tree, ready to be planted. The nobleman stopped

---

nobleman—*a man of high
rank in society*

sapling—*a young tree*

to watch, and after a few minutes he called out to the old man, "What kind of tree are you planting there, my good man?"

The old man wiped his brow and picked up the sapling. "This is a fig tree, sir," he said.

"A fig tree?" cried the astonished nobleman. "Why, how old are you, may I ask?"

"I am ninety years old," said the other.

"What!" cried the nobleman. "You are ninety years old, and you plant a tree that will take years and years to give fruit?"

"Why not?" replied the old man.

The nobleman pointed to the tree. "Surely you don't expect to live long enough to get any benefit from the hard work you are doing with this sapling!"

The old man leaned on his shovel and looked around the garden. Then he smiled and said, "Tell me, sir, did you have figs when you were a boy?"

"Certainly." The nobleman sounded puzzled. "Why?"

The old man smiled again. "Then tell me this," he said. "Who planted the trees from which those figs were picked?"

The nobleman hesitated. "Why—why, I don't know."

"You see, sir," the old man continued, "our forefathers planted trees for us to enjoy, and I am doing the same for those who come after me. How else can I repay my debt to those who lived before me?"

The nobleman was silent for a moment and then said, "You are very wise, old man, and I have been foolish."

"Thank you, sir," said the old man. "May I ask your name?"

"It doesn't matter," said the nobleman. "You are far more important than I am. Good-by."

The old man nodded his head in farewell and began to dig again, while the nobleman clucked to his horse and rode off, one arm raised in salute to the wise old man.

Character Theme—Helpfulness & Wisdom

Thinking It Through

1. What was the old man planting in his garden?
2. Why was the nobleman so surprised to see the old man planting a fig tree?
3. What explanation did the old man give for planting the tree?

Trees

Joyce Kilmer

I think that I shall never see
A poem lovely as a tree.

A tree whose hungry mouth is prest
Against the earth's sweet flowing breast;

A tree that looks at God all day
And lifts her leafy arms to pray;

A tree that may in summer wear
A nest of robins in her hair;

Upon whose bosom snow has lain;
Who intimately lives with rain.

Poems are made by fools like me,
But only God can make a tree.

Credits